D1377634

The 21st Century

The New Age of Exploration

Fred Warshofsky

New York  The Viking Press

First published in 1969 by The Viking Press, Inc.
625 Madison Avenue, New York, N.Y. 10022

Published simultaneously in Canada by
The Macmillan Company of Canada Limited

Library of Congress catalog card number: 69-11724

Printed in U.S.A.

For Marian, Beth, and Amy,
the inheritors of the 21st century

Acknowledgments

This book had its genesis in the CBS News Television series, *The 21st Century*, sponsored by the Union Carbide Corporation. I should therefore like to acknowledge the contributions of the entire production unit of the series for their help in the preparation of this book. Although it is impossible to name everyone, I should especially like to note the contributions of Burton Benjamin, executive producer, and Isaac Kleinerman, producer, for their advice and encouragement, and Judy Towers, Tom Shachtman, and Jon Wilkman, whose initial research for the series provided a broad base for the book.

The range of topics covered made it imperative that experts check every statement for scientific accuracy. For this difficult but absolutely essential chore I should like to thank the following: Norbert Dernbach, Public Relations Officer, Brookhaven National Laboratory; Dr. Maurice Goldhaber, Director, Brookhaven National Laboratory; Lt. Comdr. Wes Larson, Public Information Officer, Deep Submergence Systems Project Office, Department of the Navy; Martin W. Nabut, Supervisor of Press Relations, Bell Laboratories; Julian Scheer, Assistant Administrator of Public Affairs, National Aeronautics and Space Administration; Stanley Schneider, Assistant to the Chairman, Atomic Energy Commission; Bruce Strasser, Executive Director of Public Relations and Publications, Bell Laboratories; Richard F. Whalen, Program Administrator, International Business Machines Corporation.

Table of Contents

Prologue: Tomorrow Is Now

In about three decades the Julian calendar followed by most of the western world will record the year 2001—the beginning of the 21st century. It is half a lifetime away for some of us, the beginnings of maturity for our children. It is, in short, an easily comprehended span of time. It is also far more than a chronological event; it is a bench mark denoting drastic and irreversible change. In that sense the 21st century is already here, for the responsibility for the events and technology that will produce that change are being formed today.

The meaning and importance of chronological time is less vital now than ever before in history. Until today, time was the mover and shaker of man's destiny. Time began for man more than a million years ago in what is now the Olduvai Gorge, a sun-blasted, desiccated slash across the face of East Africa. Once, long ago, it was a rich valley, lush with fruit and grazing land that made for good hunting and enough water to slake a thirst. It was probably here that the first creature whom anthropologists can call man arose. From the bottom of the gorge one can look upward at the history of primitive man—layer upon layer of midden heaps, serried, stone-clubbed civilizations sandwiched one atop the other for ten thousand years.

One climbs up, out of the gorge, looks back down from the top, and notes the harshness with which a changing climate and a parade of arriving and departing glaciers have savaged the face of the East African plain. It seems so short a time, and it all passed before man had learned to write, even before man knew how to speak. It was but an eyeblink of time, and yet it allowed nature to work its wondrous way, selecting a trait here, discarding a dozen there, trying constantly to pick exactly that subtle and unique chemical arrangement that would add up to brain and bone, antibody and phagocyte, that would lead to survival against the greatest of earth's creatures and its smallest. And even these changes, occurring over perhaps a hundred million years, had been stewing in a biological pot that had been aboil for perhaps a billion years. The major ingredient was time, aeons in which nature could experiment with millions of designs, and then still more time for slow-witted, even slower-moving man to try out this superb equipment that had furnished him with the tools of survival.

Now, modern man, Homo sapiens, the inheritor of all this painstaking care lavished over the millennia, has arrived upon the scene. From the vantage point of today he towers above his history and looks back from virtually Olympian heights upon a million years of his past.

To look ahead from the last third of the 20th century is to glimpse a tomorrow that has virtually passed before it has arrived. The deliberate, slow pace of nature has been augmented, and we are rushing at tomorrow so swiftly our future seems already to have arrived. Events, inventions, mores, moralities, all slide and change so swiftly as to become one indistinguishable blur. And over all is the incredible speed of a developing technology that will revolutionize our lives more than all the "isms" of all the fire-eaters of history ever succeeded in doing.

From our vantage point it is possible to extrapolate from certain seemingly well-rooted trends and technologies and thus gain a glimpse, at the very least, of the possible tomorrows that await us. The increasing sophistication of our rocketry, for example, augurs well for a continued assault on space. At the same time, we have virtually run out of frontiers on land and will probably turn at long last to the sea that blankets seven tenths of the earth's surface. We shall ask more questions—of the beginnings of things, and where they are headed. We shall have far more and better tools with which to pry loose the answers from a reluctant universe. "How did it all begin?" is certain to be a major intellectual question at which the cosmologists of the 21st century will launch themselves with all the exotica that a space-oriented society can offer. X-ray astronomy, gamma-ray astronomy, orbiting astronomical observatories, and the stable, atmosphere-free far side of the moon as the finest of all observatories, will be the disciplines and the platforms we shall use to peer out into space and back into time to the origin of all things.

And what might man find there? No one today has any answers. We can safely say only that the questions will be raised and countless voyages in search of answers will be undertaken. In truth, the 21st century will probably be a new age of exploration, as men ask the questions they have always asked, but to which they never before had the means of seeking the answers.

The 21st century will surely provide those means. Already, the laser, the computer, and atomic energy have found their ways into the lives of most Americans. Whether it be in welding microcircuits for our telephones, turning the wheels of our generators, or computing our income tax, the tools of tomorrow are already being used for the tasks of today. These same tools will be applied to new tasks in the 21st century, tasks we cannot even conceive of today. But the gap between today and tomorrow is narrowing at such an incredible rate that it is no longer necessary to discern these jobs. One need only see the device to determine its awesome possibilities.

In every area of human endeavor the future offers dazzling capabilities for exploring and understanding ourselves and the world about us. The question is in fact not so much what will we learn, but rather what shall we do with the incredible mountains of knowledge we are at this very moment heaping together. Shall we explore the other planets of the solar system or the depths of our oceans? Shall we control the weather or the human mind?

In all probability, we shall accept every challenge the human mind can find, in deepest space or inside its own cortex. These are simply broad areas of probability, yet it is to these only that we can look in the hope of seeing where we are headed. For the technological avalanche threatens to inundate us, interposing its gadgetry between us and the reality of a new form of life, fashioned and governed not simply by human beings and their values and desires but by an incredibly complex machinery that seems bent on perpetual motion for its own sake. Technology begets an ever more elaborate technology, and in the process it creates problems that could not have been foreseen. Moreover, the solution to these problems lies in creating a still more sophisticated technology. A case in point is the automobile. After Henry Ford made it practical from the technological standpoint (by mass production) and economically feasible (by paying his workers five dollars a day, enough to buy one), the automobile became a phenomenal success. No one could have foreseen then that it would become part of the very fabric of life in the 20th century, or that its influence would reach out far beyond the simple requirements of transportation. Who, for example, in 1903, could have foreseen that in America the automobile would kill fifty thousand people a year, that it would affect our foreign policy vis-à-vis the Middle Eastern oil producers, that it would change our sexual mores by introducing back-seat love-making, or that it would pollute the air in almost every city in America?

Thus our technology creates a whole spectrum of seemingly unrelated problems that stem from one advance and become a major factor in shaping our lives. Moreover, it creates these problems not by failing in its designed goals but by succeeding brilliantly. With every new technological development there comes a new set of unforeseen problems, and we have reached a point where we cannot afford unforeseen problems, lest they outstrip our intellectual capacity to deal with them. We will soon learn to plumb the depths of the human gene and so present to nature on a molecular level our demands for the future of man. Shall we eliminate diabetes from the human race by substituting one gene for another? But what effect might that have on the other genes within the constellation of chromosomes that make up the blueprint of man? Can we determine the effect of changes we will make in the heart of a molecule or in the atomic nucleus of a star? The 21st century will foster great change, but it will also demand extreme caution and scientific discipline. For the targets of exploration are almost within our grasp, and the tools that will extend our reach are also close at hand. We shall pursue knowledge; it will be the preoccupation of 21st-century man. The only questions remaining concern the uses to which such knowledge will be put and the price we must pay for it.

Part One: The Tools of Tomorrow

When looms weave by themselves, man's slavery will end.

—ARISTOTLE

1
The Computer Revolution

It has been said that without the computer the space program would be impossible. The fact is, that without the computer the 21st century would be impossible. The incredible technology we are building, the complexity and the knowledge we are amassing on the way toward the creation of that not-so-far-off 21st century, are all beyond the unaided mind and muscle of man. More than any other single invention, perhaps even more than the wheel, the computer offers a promise so dazzling and a threat so awesome that it will forever change the direction and meaning of our lives.

"The computer," declares Dr. Jerome B. Weisner, Provost of the Massachusetts Institute of Technology, "with its promise of a million-fold increase in man's capacity to handle information, will undoubtedly have the most far-reaching social consequences of any contemporary technical development. The potential for good in the computer and the danger inherent in its misuse exceed our ability to imagine. . . . We have actually entered a new era of evolutionary history, one in which rapid change is a dominant consequence. Our only hope is to understand the forces at work and to take advantage of the knowledge we find to guide the evolutionary process."

Computers today are running our factories, determining our income tax, planning our cities, teaching our children, and forecasting the possible futures we may be heir to. Despite its increasingly pervasive role, few people outside the scientific community know anything at all about the computer's capabilities or potentials. To most, it is a black box, a mechanical brain, a thinking machine that in some mysterious fashion is beginning to take over many of the tasks that were once done by men. And so it is, but there is no mystery about

This computer, installed on board an oceanographic research ship, will enable scientists to perform immediate analysis of data while still at sea—a valuable asset for oceanographers on long expeditions. *(Scripps Institution of Oceanography)*

it. The computer is after all only a machine, designed and built by men to do man's bidding. The danger from computers lies not within the machine but within man and the manner in which he uses the computer.

In the new age of exploration the computer is solving in milliseconds the problems a generation of mathematicians would need years to solve without its help. To an American public already jaded by manned space flights telecast into their living rooms, the elegant mathematics of the countdown, the billions of calculations needed for each launching, all performed in milliseconds, are a commonplace—if they are given any thought at all. But the fact is that every lift-off, every photograph of the far side of the moon, has been accomplished only after a mountain of mathematics has been built as a theoretical launching pad.

And now, the computer goes aloft with the astronauts, for the complexities of orbital flights and the intricacies of rendezvous in space, a maneuver that must be perfected before man can land on the moon or venture to Mars and back, are beyond man's mental-reflex capacity. The enormousness of the problems of space maneuvering first arose on the flight of Gemini-Titan IV in 1965. The mission plan was for the GT-IV vehicle to rendezvous with its discarded booster. But each burst of the thruster rockets raised the spacecraft higher and higher above the target, while wasting the precious fuel. As the orbits grew even farther apart, the distance separating GT-IV from its booster opened up still more, and at last the attempt was abandoned.

Man, tumbling about in his thin, metal-skinned spacecraft, simply cannot perform the complex mathematical functions needed to bring his vehicle alongside another object in space. It would be like trying to drive your car into the garage while the garage moves away from you and the road that usually leads to it has vanished and you yourself have no more idea of which end of the car is the front than if you were seated in a closed, black box.

The traditional guideposts of earth are not found in space. There is no gravitational pull to remind us at all times which end is up or down. There are no straight lines, like roads, to drive along. There is no air rushing past the tail surfaces against which a rudder can push and so turn a plane to a desired course, and there is no absolute speed—only relative motion, the difference between velocity of the spacecraft and the speed of the target as it whirls through its own orbit. Under such conditions it is impossible to "eyeball" the spacecraft—to mark visually the proper course along which to thrust with rockets and so make a rendezvous in space.

The answers to such complexities now come

Without the computer, the space program would be impossible. This roomful of equipment at the Goddard Space Flight Center in Greenbelt, Maryland, houses the world's fastest and most powerful computer of the 1960s. *(IBM)*

from an electronic eye, radar, and a thinking machine, a computer the size of a hatbox which will perform in seconds the calculations it would take a man working twenty-four hours a day every day for nine years to make. For that is the weight of mathematics that must be solved in the absence of the "feel" the driver of a car has that enables him to make the intuitive adjustments of wheel, gas, and brake that will bring his car safely into the garage. In the case of a trip to the moon, the garage will be an Apollo spacecraft waiting in lunar orbit to dock with the landing module before undertaking the long leg of the journey back to earth.

The small, fifty-nine-pound computer, which

From this TV-monitor the entry and progress of a dozen different computer jobs can be checked as they run simultaneously through the giant computer. Its speed of computation enables this computer to do up to 16.6 million additions a second. *(IBM)* takes up only one cubic foot of space in the vehicle, will do all of the mathematics needed to solve one billion different space-maneuvering, navigation, and re-entry problems. Moreover, it translates the answers into simple numbers that tell the astronaut the attitude to which he must bring the spacecraft before firing the thrusters, and indicate to him exactly how long they must be fired.

Even before a rocket is launched, it is flown from ten to a hundred times through space—computer-simulated space—on flights constructed of mathematical symbols, on trajectories built of information bits, encountering hazards that are numbers without menace. For one of the computer's greatest assets is its ability to simulate one or a million variants of the same theme. "What if?" is the question the computer can answer accurately, swiftly, and over and over again. From this variety of possibilities, a trip from the earth to the moon can be simulated as often as necessary, with every possible trajectory plotted and every mile of the journey through space marked with symbolic signposts that will provide assurance that, mathematically at least, man has traveled this way before. The specter of tragedy that has always hung over the by-guess-and-by-God trials of man is sharply reduced by computer simulation.

The computer can do far more than simulate the mechanics of space flight; it can furnish accurate models of life itself. In computer simulation, then, there may come the great breakthrough needed to convert the inexact social sciences—the studies of man as a social being—into an exact science. For the sociologist the problem has always been the lack of an adequate yardstick by which to measure and count. The one absolutely essential

Automatic finishing machines deliver hot-rolled steel sheets at America's first completely computer-controlled steel mill, where hot slabs of steel are rolled into long sheets ranging in thickness from 0.047 to 0.500 inches. *(Bethlehem Steel Corporation)*

tool of science is the measuring device. Anything that can be counted, measured, quantified, can be studied with scientific accuracy.

Thus it becomes possible to perform controlled experiments, in which every factor that goes in is known in advance and the answers that come out are then valid. This could never before be done in the social sciences, because the experimenter was inevitably a part of the experiment and therefore changed the conditions of the experiment. Unlike the physicist, who could stand outside the experiment and simply note the results, the sociologist was, inevitably, an added factor who simply could not stand outside. Computer simulation allows the social scientist to remove himself in effect from the experiment. Thus each of the variables can be fed into the computer to be measured and counted as part of a simulated study.

"With computer simulation," says Columbia University sociologist Daniel Bell, "you can have a series of problems in which you can figure out all the ramifications, all the permutations and combinations, and do it very quickly and know the different combinations that are at stake. So you can use it really as a means of controlled experiment. You can get a computer model of a city and play out all the different effects, so that if you decide, for example, to relocate traffic in one way you can trace out very quickly, on the model, the effects on industry locations, residential densities, and the like. And more important, when you have alternative plans of this kind you can then choose, and that, it seems to me, is the fundamental aspect of all such notions of planning. It allows you to have a sense of wider choice, to see therefore, the consequences of it and say, I prefer this scheme rather than another."

And just what are the schemes we prefer? The computer is already building for us a world one scarcely recognizes as bearing any great relationship with yesterday's. One need only walk into an industrial plant, the great employer and despoiler of men in years past, to see what enormous changes have been wrought. At Burns Harbor, Indiana, for example, a Bethlehem Steel mill is run by a computer. Within its memory banks are the instructions needed to turn a red-hot slab of twelve-inch-thick steel into a shimmering, paper-thin ribbon a quarter of a mile long. The mill was designed around the computer. Its giant roughing stands and hydraulic sprays are computer directed and controlled. It is a complex of intricate machinery moving to the beat of another machine—the computer. The technology of one machine running another has been given a label—process control—a phrase that fits neatly into the pastiche of language that has become the jargon of computers. To go even further into the jargon, the computer at Burns Harbor is said to be on line—that is, it receives feedback from sensors on the production line. The computer compares these signals with the instructions stored in its memory, records its findings on punched paper tape, and transmits a return signal to the production machinery to adjust the gauges, dials, etc., that will in turn raise or lower the temperature, increase or decrease the amount of pressure on the slabs of steel, or otherwise adjust the process to deliver the desired finished product.

This is the main innovation, the direct control of the computer over the steel through every phase of its production in this mill. The men—the puddlers, the rollers, the dial twisters—disappeared from the production line years ago when steel making was first automated. Now, a handful of men monitor the information that goes to and from the computer.

Process control has done something else as well: it has given the limited brain of the computer muscles of enormous power. This new-found combination will have profound effects on our future, for just as the industrial revolution replaced man's muscles as an economic asset, so the computer threatens to make valueless the menial mentality.

Mathematician Norbert Wiener, who more than anyone else became a full-time philosopher of the computer, put it this way: "Let us consider the activity of the little figures which dance on top of a music box. They move in accordance with a pattern, but it is a pattern which is set in advance, and in which the past activity of the figures has practically nothing to do with the pattern of their future activities. There is a message, indeed, but it goes from the machinery of the music box to the figures and stops there. The figures themselves have no trace of communication with the outer world, except this one-way stage of communication with the pre-established mechanism of the music box. They are blind, deaf, and dumb and cannot vary their activity in the least from the conventional pattern."

So, too, was man on the endlessly repetitive production line, reduced to mute and unfeeling action. The computer will indeed take over from man, but it will do those jobs that a man should not have had to do in the first place. The result will be an increasing sophistication on the part of the computer, a gradual, but inevitable take-over of increasingly complex jobs that were once considered the exclusive province of man. At the *Miami Herald*, in Florida, a computer takes a reporter's typewritten story, arranges the words into columns, counts characters, and even hyphenates words, at the rate of twelve thousand lines an hour. It translates the information into holes in a paper tape and then uses the tape to run a linotype machine. The computer, not a linotype operator, then sets type at the rate of eight hundred and forty lines an hour. The best a highly skilled human operator can do is two hundred and fifty lines an hour. The man, a skilled craftsman not a production-line zombie, has been replaced by a machine. The consequences could be devastating or they could prove beneficial in the extreme. In this case the retrained linotype operators run the computers. In other cases men have simply been dislodged—victims of what is glibly called technological unemployment.

This is the social component to the equation that must be considered along with the dollars and cents of mere production efficiency. It is perhaps best expressed in an apocryphal story of the union delegate being shown through an auto company's newest automated engine-block plant. "You'll have a hard time collecting union dues from these machines," says the plant manager. "Yes," admits the union man, "but you'll have a harder time getting them to buy cars."

The social equation will be noted, probably by a computer dealing with the problem, and perhaps be solved with a justice men have come to expect from today's society. There will, despite the encroachments of the computer, still be jobs for men. Just what these jobs will be is not easy to forecast, but it is not necessary to do so. This is a case where the computer will provide. By taking over tasks that once demanded the application of a man's mind, the machine forces us into new roles, new jobs that require thought processes a computer cannot supply.

11

What the computer does, however, it does marvelously well. How is the incredibly rapid and efficient calculation possible? How does the computer do it?

There are two types of computers, the analogue and the digital. The analogue computer can trace its lineage as far back as the ancient Greek astronomer Hipparchus, who used a form of analogue to make measurements of the moon and its distance from the earth. Basically, today's analogue computer is a device for measuring such physical quantities as lengths and voltages and, through a mechanical linkage, exhibiting the measurement as a numerical value. A familiar example of the analogue computer is the automobile speedometer. The physical quantities it measures are the rotation and diameter of the car's wheels. These measurements are then spelled out for the driver as miles per hour and distance the car has traveled. Although it is a reasonably accurate tool for the job, the speedometer does not provide an exact value. It is, at best, a close approximation of actual speed.

As a result of this built-in imprecision, no matter how slight, the analogue computer is limited to special classes of problems. When most people say computer today, they mean the digital computer. It is a marvel of precision and accuracy, for it works with specific units rather than approximations. The lineage of the digital computer is far older than that of the analogue. The human hand was the original digital computer. With it, man could count and by counting understand all sorts of problems. The modern electronic digital computer is not very different. It has but two fingers and counts with incredible speed using only two numbers—the one and zero of what mathematicians call the binary system.

The counting ability of the computer is used to feed it information. But first the information is translated into a code, the two-fingered logic of the computer.

The information is then stored in a memory bank made of magnets. The direction in which electrical signals run through the magnets means one or zero, yes or no, off or on. Each magnet contains one piece of information called a bit. A large computer system can store hundreds of millions of such information bits.

But information by itself is useless. The computer must be told what to do with it—to add, subtract, multiply, or divide the coded pulses stored in its memory. Parts of that memory contain instructions, prepared by a human brain, that provide the computer with the road to follow in order to solve a problem. These instructions are called the program.

What makes the computer different from all other machines—an adding machine can also do arithmetic—is that the computer can modify its instructions. If a problem cannot be solved by following one route, the computer can search its memory for another set of instructions until a solution is found. And it does all this at superhuman speeds. The on-off switching of the computer's logic circuits has been clocked at a billionth of a second. That is to one second what one second is to thirty years.

But the computer cannot actually think. It performs all of its functions by rote. Once an answer is achieved, another program within the memory tells the computer how to display the solution, to type it out on paper, display it as pictures or words on a television screen, or perhaps even to speak the answer in words a man can hear.

The computer is revolutionizing medicine. In addition to interpreting electrocardiograms and aiding in diagnosis of disease, it is taking care of the countless details of patient care in the hospital.

Information is simultaneously the computer's fuel, its raw material, and its product; it is its single and total *raison d'être*. In some fields this ability to manipulate facts—to make thousands of comparisons between incoming information and information already conveniently stored in a memory and then make predetermined choices based on those comparisons—is an invaluable asset. The medical profession, awash in paperwork, harried by growing personnel shortages and demands for patient care, has turned to the computer to prevent a breakdown in medical care. According to Dr. G. Octo Barnett, Director of the Laboratory of Computer Science at the Massachusetts General Hospital in Boston, "the computer will improve the quality of medical care and make better use of our limited medical manpower base."

The hospital is the focal point of all of medicine's problems and successes, and it is on this ground that the doctor and computer link up initially. For in the hospital the major battle is no longer for life, but to move mountains of information. Melville H. Hodge, Assistant Director of Information Systems at Lockheed Missiles and Space Company, which is studying hospital administration, estimates that as much as thirty per cent of all hospital costs go for manual information handling. One hospital in the Lockheed study was found to go through twelve distinct information transfers for a single laboratory test order.

At the Monmouth Medical Center in Long Branch, New Jersey, a prototype of the computerized hospital of tomorrow is being developed today. Patient care is under the watchful electronic memory of a massive computer system called HIS, for hospital information system. HIS links twenty hospital stations to a central computer—an IBM

This computerized system at Monmouth Medical Center in New Jersey will assign patients to beds, schedule laboratory tests, offer the results, order medication, and even bill the patient for his hospital stay.

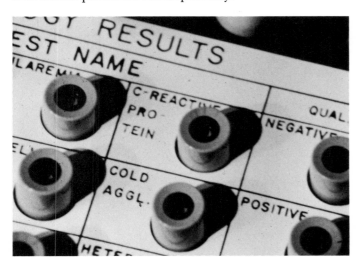

system 360. Every detail of patient care is punched into the computer from the terminals—medical history, the cost of drugs, diagnostic tests, doctors' special orders, requests for television sets—to free doctors, nurses, and administrators to concentrate on their main chores. The patient enters the system in the admissions office, and as the data is punched into the computer, it searches its memory for records of a previous visit. It orders standard blood tests, typing out the order on a terminal in the blood laboratory, and even assigns the incoming patient to a room. Every order into the system is checked against a variety of factors.

Drug orders are subjected to a special computer scrutiny. Each prescription is given a "relative dosage check," which compares the prescribed medication with the patient's weight, age and the amount of the drug he has received in the past. Absolute limits for adults and children, predetermined by the hospital's pharmaceutical committee, are also in the computer program.

Every drug ordered, meal served, or bed made is noted by the computer, which adjusts the hospital's various inventories and housekeeping requirements and, of course, also bills the patient. But the computer can do far more in medicine than merely keep track of drugs, bills, and beds. It is now being called upon to perform complex diagnostic duties.

At Mount Sinai Hospital in New York, for example, it interprets electrocardiograms, the complex wave forms that are the pictorial representation of the electrical activity of the human heart. More than fifty million ECG's are made in the United States each year, and their interpretation is not only time consuming but also subject to error, for not all doctors can draw the correct conclusions. But Mount Sinai uses a computer, programed by expert cardiologists to diagnose ECG's swiftly and accurately. For the doctor, such a computer program is the equivalent of having the world's greatest specialists on immediate call as consultants.

The idea of putting the best medical brains into computer programs has not escaped IBM's Dr. Frederic J. Moore, who is leading the development of a clinical decision support (CDS) system which will eventually answer ninety-five per cent of all the questions raised in adult medical practice. By punching in the pertinent data—age, weight, sex, temperature, blood pressure, and any symptoms of illness, such as a sore throat and itching skin— the doctor uses the computer much as he would a consultant. A dialogue ensues between doctor and computer, the keyboard of a typewriter being used as the means of communication. The computer requests additional information, and the doctor supplies it. Then the computer thumbs its magnetic memory and supplies a list of all diseases that might account for the symptoms supplied by the doctor. If the physician requests it, the computer will also suggest the next few steps needed to further narrow the diagnosis—X-rays, chemical tests, etc.

With that information added, the computer is prepared to offer a fairly firm diagnosis and also offer the commonly accepted treatment—everything from an aspirin tablet to major surgery. The doctor, for his part, is free to accept or reject the advice. He may even argue with the computer. "Why," he may ask the machine, "didn't you consider the possibility of watchamacallit's disease?" The computer will then explain exactly why it omitted the possibility.

According to Dr. Moore, the CDS program is not meant to be a replacement for the thinking physician, but rather it is a valuable tool to assist him. "It can remind him of things he might otherwise overlook and put at his fingertips the pertinent facts from a body of useful medical knowledge that is already far too large to be kept in any one doctor's mind."

Much of this towering mountain of medical information is stored at the National Library of Medicine in Bethesda, Maryland, which adds to its monumental information pile by indexing almost one quarter of a million technical articles plus thousands of books and monographs each year. To keep up with this overwhelming tide of information is simply beyond the resources of the conventional card catalogue.

The computer has been brought into the breach to run a system called MEDLARS, for medical literature analysis and retrieval system. The MEDLARS computer prints out a weighty catalogue of information, the *Index Medicus*, which lists an average of fourteen thousand new scientific articles every month. MEDLARS also provides a demand bibliography. Doctors simply send in a subject heading, and the computer will come back with a complete and up-to-date bibliography in reply to the demand.

Other specialized fields are also developing computerized storage and retrieval systems to manage the incredible flow of new knowledge being generated by an increasingly complex technology. The American Chemical Society, for example, has a computer service that monitors and abstracts almost one and a half million papers on chemistry a year. The chemist's problem may be unique. One estimate is that eighty-five per cent of man's total store of chemical knowledge consists of information on the nature and properties of compounds. There are now upwards of four million

17

known chemical compounds, with new ones being made, discovered, and reported at the rate of one hundred thousand a year. To correlate the structural features and the chemical and physical properties of each of these compounds is simply beyond the scope of human analysis and can now only be done by the computer.

In every field of human endeavor the body of knowledge is being swollen to the bursting point by a flood of new facts, which by their very existence help to generate still more facts until the mass of information threatens to engulf us.

But the problem can be controlled and reduced to usable proportions by the computer. All that is required is a human mind at one end of the system with enough sense to say, "Halt! I've learned just about all I want to know about wickets." This will become the touchstone to the computerized library of the 21st century, in which requests for information will be answered instantly and as fully as the user wants.

But still faster means of getting at computer-stored information must be developed. The problems of communicating with the computer are becoming increasingly apparent. Punch cards, typewriter terminals, and paper tapes all demand special codes and computer languages. It's as if you had to decode every word in this book before its meaning could be understood. Such a situation can no longer be accepted, for computers already calculate at a blinding pace, and their speeds are steadily increasing.

The great leap forward in computer technology was attained in 1947, when three Bell Laboratory scientists developed the transistor. Transistors can perform all of the functions of vacuum tubes but are flea-sized by comparison and require only a

DATE Dec 24 1947
CASE No. 38139-7

in it was determined that the power gain was the order of effect of 18 or greater. Various people witnessed this test and listened (were present) of whom some were the following R.B. Gibney, H. R. Moore, J. Bardeen G. L. Pearson, W Shockley, H. Fletcher R. Bown. Mrs. H. R. Moore assisted in setting up the circuit and the demonstration occurred on the afternoon of Dec 23 1947

Read & understood by
G. L. Pearson Dec 24, 1947
H. R. Moore Dec 24, 1947

◀ ▲ Entry in the notebook of scientist Walter H. Brattain, recording the discovery of the transistor effect in 1947, for which Brattain and his two collaborators later shared a Nobel Prize. *(Bell Telephone Laboratories)*

fraction as much power to operate. The transistor is made of a semiconductor, a crystal that conducts electricity better than glass, though not as well as metal. The manufacture of a transistor starts with a single pure crystal of semiconductor, such as germanium. The addition of very small amounts of a chemical impurity such as arsenic introduces excess electrons into the crystal lattice. These electrons can move easily to carry electricity. Other atomic impurities such as boron soak up electrons from the lattice and thus create deficiencies, or holes, where there are no electrons. The hole, in effect, is a positive charge, the opposite of the negatively charged electron. Both holes and electrons skip through the material with ease.

Arsenic- and boron-doped crystals are sliced into wafers and then sandwiched together so that alternating layers containing either free electrons or holes face each other. Holes and electrons, carrying opposite electrical charges, are attracted to each other and a few drift across the junction, creating an electrical field.

By adding electrical contact points to each of the layers in the sandwich, a transistor is created. Current flowing between two of the contact points can be controlled by sending an electrical signal to a third point. The signal can thus be amplified from fifty to forty thousand times. Moreover, the current keeps step with the incoming signal, so that when it is pumped back out again, the signal is a precisely amplified image of the original signal.

By 1955 the transistor was replacing the vacuum tube in computers, shrinking their size and increasing their speed. The transition from vacuum tubes to transistors, which scaled the computer down from the dinosaur to the dachshund, was but the

19

first step, according to one computer expert. Integrated circuits that combine both amplifiers and other electrical components on slivers of material far smaller than even the transistor are shrinking the size of the computer still further. The integrated circuits conserve space, and they also save time and the effort of linking up individual components. This means that a quarter-inch chip containing five or six complete circuits can move information across its route faster than a transistorized circuit because every element within it is closer than are the elements of transistors. On the horizon is yet another shrinkage, which will be made possible by a process, still undeveloped, called large-scale integration, or LSI. An LSI chip will be only a tenth of an inch square and will carry as many as one hundred circuits. The difference between an LSI chip and an integrated circuit chip may seem like hairsplitting, but on such negligible differences are built great strides in computer technology.

The limiting speed on computers is the speed of light. Computer engineers used this fact to create a standard measure—the light-foot—by which to clock computer speeds. It is defined as the distance, about twelve inches, that light travels in a billionth of a second.

Miniaturization will narrow the gap between circuits and so reduce the number of light-feet that must be traversed through the logic circuits. But there are still other limitations that must be overcome before computer processing will be rapid enough to satisfy the demands of perfectionists. Computers must still be programed for every action they take. How quickly the programer can tell it what to do becomes a major drag on computer speeds. The computer would follow each step in the program in rather plodding fashion—plod-

A capsule history of computers can be seen in the comparative size of these three computer components—a vacuum tube, a transistor with its protective can, and at lower right, a tiny silicon integrated circuit, containing the equivalent of twenty-two transistors and other components. *(Bell Telephone Laboratories)*

This computer microcircuit, magnified several hundred times, actually measures less than a twentieth of an inch. *(Bell Telephone Laboratories)*

ding, that is, for a machine that has an engineered capability to perform a million calculations a second.

The time lag can be shortened by linking up different computers and designing more efficient devices to jam information in and pull it out of the machine, but the basic limitation of the step-by-step program remains.

A means around that roadblock is called parallel processing. Developed by Daniel L. Slotnick, of the University of Illinois, parallel processing calls for a master control and a few hundred arithmetic and memory units to do the basic computing. Instead of solving a problem by following the step-by-step instructions of the program, the arithmetic and memory units will break the main problem down into a number of smaller problems that will be solved simultaneously.

Parallel processing is going into a newly designed experimental computer called ILLIAC IV. Named for the University of Illinois, where it was designed, it will be built with large-scale integration and so be a fourth-generation computer. (ILLIAC IV is not on the scene, however, for ILLIAC III has not yet been finished.) Adding parallel processing to ILLIAC IV will also give it blinding speed, even for a computer. Slotnick envisions the machine as being capable of performing about one billion calculations a second. That's five hundred times faster than present-day computers and, according to engineers, "one hundred times faster than any computer known to be in development."

The incredibly rapid speeds we are approaching will be of little value without a corresponding increase in the speed with which we can get at the computer-generated information. One new approach, called graphics, uses the cathode-ray tube

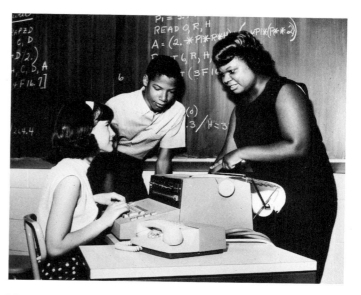

The computer may mystify many adults, but their children will use it as naturally as their parents use paper and pencil. These students at Wagner Junior High School in Philadelphia listen intently as their mathematics teacher explains the use of a computer to help solve homework problems. *(IBM)*

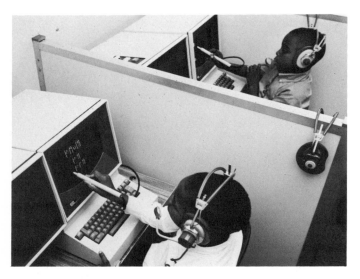

A computer, with a visual-display unit upon which the computer can draw or print out messages, is used at the Brentwood School in East Palo Alto, California, to instruct youngsters in arithmetic. *(IBM)*

At the UCLA Medical Center this graphics-display unit connected to a computer is used to study a microscopic X-ray of a chromosome. *(University of California, Los Angeles)*

—the picture tube of your TV set—to display the information pictorially. A light pen—actually an electronic pointer—can be touched to the screen, and conversation between man and machine can be accomplished. For example, the computer can flash a series of options on its screen. The scientist selects the one he wants by touching it with a light pen. The great advantage of these so-called graphic computers is in solving design problems and in coping with any trial-and-error situation. For the computer can take the mathematics of bridge building, for example, reduce it to the lines of a drawing, and display it on its screen. It is all made possible by a program that can position the electron beam of the cathode-ray tube to any of more than one million points on the screen in millionths of a second. The computer does the menial arithmetic of reducing soaring design to scale and permits the designer to concentrate on esthetics.

The General Motors Corporation is now testing a prototype man-computer design system to see whether cars can be designed in this fashion. Called DAC-1, for design augmented by computers, it may be able to slash the long lead time—now up to three years—needed to convert the stylist's concept of a new model into a final product coming off the assembly line.

The graphic computer offers the most flexible means of communication between man and machine yet developed. For example, the designer can draw a car roof on the screen with his light pen. The computer will do the mathematics required to straighten out the lines and, in effect, present a draftman's version of the designer's idea. The computer will then offer a variety of options to the designer—"front view, rear view, cross section," and so on. All the designer need do is touch his

By adding to the computer's display program, it is possible to add the dimension of depth to the graphic image. A 3-D program and a stereoscope mounted in front of the screen produce a realistic three-dimensional image. *(Brown University)*

light pen to the appropriate choice, and the computer does the rest. Similarly, the designer can circle any part of the drawing on the screen with his pen and request a blow-up—a large-scale drawing of just that part he has circled.

The end product of this man-machine design team is not a series of drawings on paper but a set of equations that precisely define every point of the design. Eventually, these symbols will be fed to the production line machinery, which will translate the symbols into the steel and glass forms of automobiles.

If the graphic computer has proven a boon to the designers and engineers, it may become the handmaiden of the more traditional arts as well. One Bell Laboratories computer engineer named Michael Noll is also a balletomane. He was struck by the problem of the choreographer who is in the position of needing a full *corps de ballet* to execute the creative idea for a new dance. Even when finished, the work remains only in the minds and bodies of the dancers. It is as if a composer could not write down his music and had instead to tell every member of a symphony orchestra of the melody in his head and how to play it. Then, when the final orchestration had been achieved, it was still not written down, but rather, each musician simply remembered his own part.

Mike Noll has replaced the dancers with a computer. "Instead of using the dancers as his choreographic instrument," he explains, "the choreographer interacts with the computer during the creative process. Stick-figure representations of the dancers appear in some form of three dimensional display on the face of an electronic display tube. The choreographer, by manipulating different buttons on the console, controls the movement and progress of the work. Different movements might be stored in the computer's memory and put together at will. Individual movement restrictions for each dancer could even be introduced into the process. Various elements of chance and randomness could be used at the discretion of the choreographer."

Tentative use of the computer in the arts has been going on for some years now and will probably continue. The computer has generated poetry, music, playlets, and novel plots, but none have been more than pale imitations of the works that come from human creativity. Man, it seems, is still the ultimate artistic creator (not including nature, of course), and his technological devices must still be considered more as the media than as the creator. Thus, the computer may never compose great symphonic music, but it might join the orchestra as a new instrument. Each musical note or sound can be described mathematically on punch cards. The cards are then fed into a computer that has been programed to generate a sequence of numbers that describe the wave form of the sound. The numbers are represented by patterns of small magnetized spots on a magnetic tape. This digital information is then converted to another magnetic sound track that when played on an ordinary tape recorder produces musical sounds.

If a computer can generate sounds that are melodic enough to be called musical, then it seems quite reasonable to assume that the computer "voice" might be induced to speak in words that could be understood by a man. Thus, man-machine communication might become conversational instead of merely the gestures possible with the graphic mode. For some specific tasks, such as giving stock market reports, the computer talks with the prerecorded voices of people. A vocabulary of pretaped voices is put into the computer, which simply selects the words and numbers required—"AT&T, 52½." This is merely simple parroting of information with a borrowed voice. But what about a computer that can really talk, that can form words with its own electronic vocal cords?

Such a device is being made at Bell Laboratories by Cecil H. Coker. Coker has placed within the computer memory a geometric description of the various positions assumed by the five articulators of the vocal tract—the tongue, lips, jaw, palate, and pharynx—when they make specific sounds. X-ray motion pictures of people talking were first obtained to see these positions. Their geometry was described mathematically and graphically, for the computer produces an outline of the vocal tract on an oscilloscope at the same time it "speaks" a given sound. By flicking an assortment of switches and dials, Coker can change the sound and the shape of the vocal tract simultaneously.

We speak without the necessity of thinking where to place lips, tongue, and jaw. The computer cannot; it must first think of each number needed to form a given shape for each of the five articulators. Thus, it speaks simple phrases very slowly, forming the words only after it has done the hundreds of calculations needed to copy the human speech positions. But once the vocal movements for a given word are computed and stored in its memory, the computer drops its machine drawl and speaks with the speed of human speech.

In order to make communication between man and machine as painless and easy as possible, the computer is being taught not only to speak but also to listen. The Autonetics Corporation has built a

Cecil H. Coker of the Bell Telephone Laboratories observes the geometry of the vocal tract in the production of human speech on the display unit of the computer. The lips, pharynx, and tongue are positioned on the screen to synthesize basic sounds. *(Bell Telephone Laboratories)*

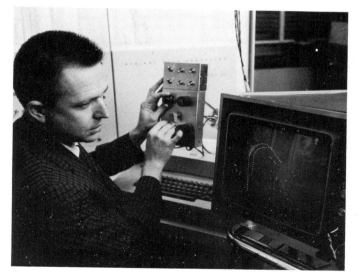

system, complete with audio analyzers and all of the complex electronics needed to give a computer "ears," that will actually hear the words spoken into its microphone. Admittedly, it has a vocabulary of only one hundred words, but it repeats them, or types them if you prefer, with an *élan* one does not expect to see in a machine. A mere one-hundred-word vocabulary might, for example, be considered a handicap in a man, but in a machine it leads to a certain unflappable quality that can only be envied. During a demonstration, the engineer spoke slowly and distinctly a handful of the computer's words, and it dutifully typed them back. But on one word it came a cropper. While counting "one, two, three," the computer typed back, "one, two, four." Whereupon the demonstrator snapped "idiot," and the computer, in a veritable machine version of British aplomb, calmly replied "Not in vocabulary."

The Autonetics computer has also been programed to translate a few foreign phrases. It does this not by recognizing the words and their English translations but simply by storing in its memories the sound patterns that constitute the phrase in a variety of languages. Whenever those patterns are picked up by the computer, it is programed to automatically print out the English equivalents. In this particular demonstration, the phrase was, "Americans rendezvous in space."

But foreign-language translation may prove to be just a bit more than the computer can handle. From the Tower of Babel on there have been countless examples of man's inability to understand man. What hope is there then for a machine to understand man, or even another machine? Apparently, the chances are far better where the machine is involved, but still not one hundred per cent. Ma-

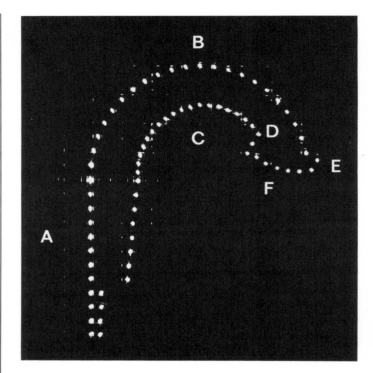

This computer-generated diagram shows a side view of: (a) pharynx, (b) palate, (c) tongue, (d) tongue tip, (e) lips, and (f) lower jaw. *(Bell Telephone Laboratories)*

This computer, developed jointly by the Systems Development Corporation and the Los Angeles Police Department, remembers the *modus operandi* of known criminals. After eye-witness reports of a crime are fed into the computer, it names all criminals in its memory using similar tactics.

chine translators would be an enormous boon, especially to science and technology. The United States Defense Department scrutinizes every new Russian and Chinese scientific, technical, and political paper with intense care. But before our scientists can evaluate them, they must be translated into English. The task is enormous, and the backlog has assumed mountainous proportions. A machine translator would obviously be a great aid.

Not long ago a machine was developed that can optically scan the written characters and print out the translation. It has a program that translates Chinese into English and English into Chinese. A no doubt apocryphal story has it that at a press demonstration the programer asked for a phrase to translate and a reporter said, "Out of sight, out of mind." The phrase was dutifully fed into the computer, which replied by printing out a string of Chinese characters.

"There," said the programer, "that means 'Out of sight, out of mind.'"

The reporter was skeptical. "I don't know any Chinese and I don't know that that means 'Out of sight, out of mind.'"

"Well," replied the engineer, "it's really quite simple. We'll ask the other program to translate the Chinese back into English."

And so once again a string of characters, this time Chinese, was fed into the computer. The translation was typed out almost immediately and it read: "invisible idiot."

Although the translation achievements of the computer still leave a great deal to be desired, the over-all problems of communication between man and machine are being solved at a rapid pace. But even the best of communications techniques are not equal to the time lag interposed by the programers and assorted experts who stand like so many barriers between the eager would-be user and the computer. Questions posed to the computer may be answered in milliseconds, but the original questioner may not get the answer for hours or days. The "real-time" use of a computer that offers the possibility of immediate answers or the establishment of a running dialogue between man and machine is usually still in the hands of only one human being. It is an extravagance few can afford.

To solve the problem, a new technique—time-sharing—may revolutionize computer use. Time-sharing permits a number of people to use a single computer at the same time from remote stations. And the services to every time-sharer are rendered at the electronic speeds of which the computer is capable. Time-sharing is made possible by the very needs that called it into being, the slow thinking of man compared to the blurring speed of calculation of the computer. All that was required was a sort of superprogram that could supervise the requests of thirty to sixty users and see that they were sent to the appropriate electronic compartment within the computer. This superprogram, or executive, as it is called, operates like a juggler with a dozen balls in the air at the same time. It assigns priorities among the users and allots each one a limited amount of actual computing time— two hundred and fifty milliseconds, for example— for each user. If the individual problem is not solved within the time period, or quantum, as it is called, it is shunted into a temporary memory, and the executive goes on to other users' problems before returning to the unanswered query.

The executive also performs a multitude of housekeeping duties that make time-sharing possible. It pulls and pushes individual client's programs out of storage and returns them when the client has finished. It prevents one user from interfering with another's program, keeps records of who uses the machines, makes corrections, and even offers tips to unskilled users. All of these tasks are performed so swiftly and efficiently that individual users are hardly aware of the fact that they are sharing the computer's time. Constant use means there are no gaps in computer time, and the individual cost of using a computer shrinks.

Eventually, the economics of time-sharing might make possible a computer terminal in everyone's home and/or office. The computer, like the telephone or electricity, may become a public utility used by almost everyone at a nominal cost.

At that point some truly startling effects on our society may be noted. Robert M. Hutchins, President of the Center for the Study of Democratic Institutions, points out that "General Electric officials envision the automation of the home through computers that will make up the wife's grocery list, remind the husband of appointments and anniversaries, pay bills, write checks, figure out income tax, and answer the telephone. Reproduction will be the only function performed by human labor."

The degree to which computers will take over human functions may frighten some and astonish others. A line of serious and sustained investigation aimed at making a computer do those things which are considered intelligent when human beings do them is being pursued vigorously in several computer laboratories. Artificial intelligence, as it is called, is intended to equip computers with the ability to solve problems of a particular type, to play games well and, in general, to act intelligently in a given situation on the basis of observation and

29

previous knowledge of how to behave in similar situations.

One of the most fascinating demonstrations of artificial intelligence can be seen at the Massachusetts Institute of Technology, where computers play chess against human players and against other computers. In theory, the computer should have a decided edge on any human opponent, for it has none of the emotional and psychological elements the human must deal with, and it can concentrate on chess without regard to anything that may intrude upon the human player's concentration. But the computer does not win every match, for it must play chess in much the same way a human being does. The chess board, with its sixty-four squares and thirty-two pieces, allows for an incalculably large number of possible moves, billions more than even a computer can keep track of. To allow the machine to play at all, it is programed to follow human thought patterns. It uses a trial-and-error method to explore only a few thousand of the billions of possible board positions. Operating within these relatively few possibilities, it determines whether or not an advantage will accrue from a particular move. If it will, the piece is moved, if not, the computer explores an alternative move until, finally, it "makes up its mind" and moves.

The built-in human quality makes it vulnerable, and so computers win a few and lose a few.

Although chess can excite the intellect, it doesn't set the heart to pounding or muscles to jumping in anticipation of physical action. And though a computer can be hooked up to run a machine, it is still a dumb-brute type of activity, the sort of thing a human being shouldn't want or have to do in the first place. But the concept of artificial intelligence goes far beyond that. A computer at MIT is

A computer playing chess against a human opponent. *(Massachusetts Institute of Technology)*

30

This computer-controlled arm-eye machine can "see" the blocks on this table and stack them in any desired order. *(Massachusetts Institute of Technology)*

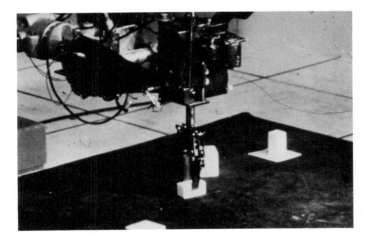

harnessed to a machine that sees with a television camera for an eye and feels with a hydraulically powered set of metal struts for an arm and hand.

The computer receives sensory information—there is a block on the table—and goes into the program to see what action it should take. Like the chess-playing computer, it too uses human thought patterns to determine cause and effect and changes in its environment. At present, all this sophisticated feedback accomplishes little more than a baby can do. It can see a block on a table, pick it up, and put it down elsewhere, and repeat the process until a tower of blocks has been built.

But there are a great many hurdles to be surmounted before machines such as this might be put to work exploring the surface of Mars or the bottom of the sea floor with the same intelligent capabilities that a latter-day Lewis or Clark would exhibit.

There are even difficulties in block building. "The main problem," explains Marvin Minsky, the scientist who developed the arm-eye machine, "is not so much picking up objects, but recognizing where they are visually. This entails taking rays of light that are coming into the camera and having the computer figure out what kinds of objects are present and what positions they are in. In this simple experiment (building a tower of blocks) the computer examines the television image, it figures out where the edges of objects are, and where the surfaces are, and from that, it constructs, you might say 'in its mind's eye,' a little model of where these objects are located out in front of the camera. Now, once it knows this, it can send instructions to the 'muscles' of the 'arm' to put the 'hand' in such a position and move the 'arm' forward, and reach down and grasp."

Such actions are a startling advance over the

31

automated equipment most people are familiar with. The end product of automation is a machine that simply performs the same job in the same way over and over again. Should the circumstances change, the machine will go on doing the same thing in the same way, even though the action is no longer necessary or correct. But this is not the case with the arm-eye machine. It can see and feel the changes made in its environment and adapt to the change. This is the focal point of the computer revolution, for it is the ability to perceive changes and cope with them that is the essence of human intelligence.

The computer has generated enormously high hopes for the future of man. Experts and visionaries are constantly quoted on the benefits the computer will bring. "Although we are barely in the second decade of electronic data processing," recently wrote General David Sarnoff, Chairman of the Board of the Radio Corporation of America, "the outlines of its influence on our culture are beginning to emerge. Far from depersonalizing the individual and dehumanizing his society, the computer promises a degree of personalized service never before available to mankind."

Dr. Simon Ramo, President of TRW Corporation, says: "The idea that man and computers are competitors is a myth. Electronic information-handling technology is, rather, giving us new ways to acquire, store, process, disseminate, and utilize the information that makes the world go round. Computers make possible improved systems of production, banking, transportation, and education. What is really happening is change—change simultaneously offering both potential benefits and potential dislocations. A mature society will work at minimizing the negative consequences in order to emphasize the benefits."

And so it goes, a cavalcade of eminently respected leaders of science, industry, and government lauding the computer and what it may do. And they are right, but there persists an air of protesting too much in their remarks, because if too many people do not understand the computer, or its possibilities, too many others understand it too well. The desire to put everything into the computer is sometimes overwhelming. The need to code everything, to reduce the facts of life to holes in a punch card and magnetized spots on a tape, can have dangerous consequences. Conformity and the need to have people and institutions conform are but the beginnings of a machine-based tyranny that can be more dictatorial than a Stalinized Russia. In the interests of bureaucratic efficiency, the computer has become the most important single factor in government. No self-respecting government bureau would dare be caught in public without its computer. Most recently, the Internal Revenue Service was able to boast that for the first time in history every federal tax return would be checked by a computer. Nothing to do with an individual or business tax return will escape the electronic eye of the computer from now on.

The cost of such a system was considerable, but its efficiency will soon earn back the outlay. No one questions the value or the need. Big government and its need for efficiency is well served by the computer. There is some question, however, of how well it serves the rights of the individuals. Plans are now underway to create a National Computer Center to store not merely tax records, but every piece of information the government pos-

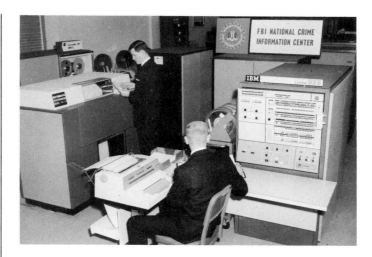

This FBI center links five cities in a computerized network that provides instant information on suspects and stolen property.

sesses about an individual. Today it is impossible to go through life without falling into the maw of the computer. Where you went to school, your grades, personality traits, credit rating, income, military service, are all recorded in one government office or another.

The plan is to combine them all into one gigantic computerized record of every man, woman, and child in the United States. It's not difficult. One tax return can be stored in just two-tenths of an inch of tape, and racks at the IRS Central Data Processing Headquarters in Martinsburg, West Virginia, already hold thousands of miles of record-laden tape.

The plan frightens a good many intelligent people who appreciate full well the capabilities and needs of a computerized government. "The centralized data bank," says Gerard Piel, publisher of the magazine *Scientific American*, "is a sufficient nightmare to contemplate. The data bank that has got your complete medical history, your complete financial history, your parking tickets, everything in it. This is a pretty appalling thing to contemplate."

Fortunately, people like Piel are doing more than simply being appalled. John McCarthy, a computer scientist at Stanford University, has proposed a sort of "Computer Bill of Rights," that would protect the individual from unwarranted bureaucratic prying. One tenet would be that every man would have the right of access to the government's file on him, so that he can challenge entries or have them deleted. Second, the computer itself would be so programed that only authorized persons would be able to get the information out of its memory. Finally, a rigorous record would be maintained of everyone who had entered the file.

But even these simple and essentially protective

ground rules don't offer complete protection. For the very people who program in the safeguards could, if so inclined, reverse or circumvent them. But McCarthy views that possibility as remote. "I think," he says, "that one can give protection against unauthorized use of this information, by, for example, making the programs that enforce the rules available to any organizations which might be formed to protect people's rights in this matter. But I don't see how we can be protected from any kind of forcible illegal usurpation, any more than we can have any physical protection against military coups. . . . It's the traditions of the country which we hope will protect us from military coups, and from the illegal use of computers."

There seems little doubt that despite the fears the central data bank will eventually become a reality. It is a logical extension of the role the computer is playing in our society. And that role is being increased at a rate that is truly astonishing. We need only count computers then, now, and tomorrow to see their growing importance.

In 1956 there were fewer than one thousand digital computers in the United States. Today there are fifty-eight thousand and eight years from now there will be more than two hundred thousand. Not only is the number of computers increasing at an incredible speed, but so too are their abilities. In the last ten years the typical computer has become ten times smaller, one hundred times faster, and one thousand times less expensive to operate. Today, the computers in America do more than twenty trillion calculations every hour; by the year 2000 that figure may have increased a hundred or even a thousandfold.

The fantastic possibilities of the computer are no longer in question. The question is, How shall we use them? There is an increasing fear of the computerized world we are building, a fear that things have been taken out of our hands by the machines. In some cases this will be true. The computer can make decisions easily, for it cannot be held accountable. It simply weighs the information it has been given and on that basis says yes or no. The computer could relieve man of the responsibility of choice. It can tell a housewife what to cook for dinner or a businessman what product to make and where to sell it. But one day it may make choices for the doctor, for the legislator, for the soldier—what drug to use, what law to pass, peace or war, heaven or hell, man or machine—these are the ultimate decisions that must be made.

In a recent student demonstration one sign read, "Do not fold, spindle, or mutilate. I am a human being."

But can we retain our humanity in the threatening shadow of the computer? Can we control the computer, which, in effect, means controlling ourselves?

If we do, we shall have command of a mighty tool, one that may help us to gain an understanding of the farthest reaches of space, the depths of the oceans, and, perhaps, of that most puzzling mystery, ourselves.

2
The Mighty Atom

A generation ago the atom connoted one thing in the popular mind—the bomb. Today the fear of a nuclear holocaust has been muted somewhat, and the atom is taking on a new meaning in the minds of the public—power. Atomic power will provide the thrust for our spaceships as they search out the mysteries of the solar system. The atom will provide much of the power that will make it possible for us to establish and maintain bases on the moon and Mars, and beneath the sea.

One of the chief aims of engineers is to translate the inherent power of the atom into a force that can be harnessed to a space vehicle. "What we are attempting to make," says Dr. Glenn T. Seaborg, Chairman of the Atomic Energy Commission, "is a flyable, compact reactor not much bigger than an office desk that will produce more power than Hoover Dam—and achieve this power from a cold start in a matter of minutes."

The prototype of such a flyable reactor is NERVA, nuclear engine for rocket vehicle application, a joint project of the Atomic Energy Commission and the National Aeronautics and Space Administration. One of its jobs might be to power a vehicle to Mars.

The principle underlying both nuclear and chemical rockets is the same. Both develop their thrust forces from the rapid expansion of hot gases. The gases spew from the throat of the exhaust nozzle and expand against its flared sides. This jetting effect pushes the rocket forward. Chemical rockets use a combination fuel, such as hydrazine, and an oxidizer. Nuclear rockets use an atomic fuel and hydrogen, which is not burned but merely heated by passing through the core of the nuclear reactor. The hydrogen is carried in liquid form inside the rocket tanks. A turbine pumps the

The nuclear rocket engine NERVA, which may become the workhorse booster of the 21st century, is seen here in a configuration at Jackass Flats, Nevada. (*Atomic Energy Commission*)

hydrogen through the reactor. The controlled fission heats the hydrogen to almost two thousand degrees centigrade. Such heat converts the hydrogen from a liquid to an extremely energetic gas, which shoots out of the thrust chamber and provides thrust to the rocket just as burned gases do in a conventional rocket.

The nuclear rocket can get a lot more mileage out of its propellant than can the conventional rocket, and so it need carry less propellant. But the engine is much heavier than a chemical rocket, and this is a decided disadvantage in lifting a payload into orbit.

The nuclear rocket is more likely to be used as a second or third stage on long interplanetary trips, where its greater efficiency will be needed. The most powerful chemical rocket now in existence, the Saturn V, develops seven and a half million pounds of thrust, but for only a few minutes. In the long jumps between planets the long firing capability of the nuclear rocket will become extremely important. The Phoebus I, a medium-sized nuclear test rocket, ran at full power—fifteen hundred megawatts—for thirty minutes. This was a startling length of time and encouraged rocket scientists to ask Congress to pay for the Phoebus II, a larger version that would produce five thousand megawatts, or two hundred and fifty thousand pounds of thrust, for the same thirty minutes. This would be the rocket that could power men to Mars once the Saturn rocket had lifted them into orbit about the earth.

The atom in harness will enable man to search out the mysteries of his solar system and perhaps reach even beyond to the nearest stars, but that is asking a great deal from even so powerful a force as atomic energy. For we are just now beginning

Nuclear power for homes and factories may soon become the rule rather than the exception. This reactor pictured under construction is called Dresden 2, the second nuclear reactor providing electrical power for the Commonwealth Edison System in Detroit. *(Babcock and Wilcox Company)*

to fathom its energy potentials. The atom was long thought to contain a vast amount of energy, but no one knew just how to liberate it. The attempt became a race after 1939 when a pair of German scientists, Fritz Strassmann and Otto Hahn, split the atom for the first time. From that moment on, the specter of the bomb hung over the world, and World War II closed when the nightmare became a reality in the skies over Hiroshima and Nagasaki.

But explosive power is but one form, and a very wasteful one, of atomic energy. The true power is harnessed in a nuclear reactor, a sort of controlled bomb that is engineered and weighted with safety devices designed to make an explosion almost impossible, and should that unlikely event occur, to insure that the ultimate product of disaster would be steam and not radioactivity, provided the containment shell is not breached.

The atomic reactor will become essential to life in the 21st century. The rise of civilization can be described as a search for more and cheaper power. A civilization's only real wealth is its source of energy, for all else, including its culture and its comfort, is dependent upon it. Today we are using energy at a prodigious rate, and by so doing we chew up the vast bulk of the supplies that fuel it. Most of our power comes from the burning of fossil fuels—coal and oil—and from running water. But every time we burn something we pollute the air and diminish our natural stockpile. Even the vast new deposits of gas and oil that have been discovered in the North Sea and those that are yet to be found in other offshore areas may not be able to supply all the needs of a 21st-century society. Today the United States, with only six per cent of the world's population, uses fifty per cent of the world's energy. As the rest of the world begins to match

View of a reactor operating floor during loading of the graphite-clad fuel elements in the reactor core. *(General Dynamics)*

40

our technological achievements, and as our own technology grows still more advanced, the demand for energy will become a clamor. Although the population of the earth may only double by 2001, the consumption of energy throughout the world will be five times as large. To supply the demand, we may have to build nuclear power plants at a rate of one a month from now until the year 2001.

Just a few years ago such a pace would have been considered absurd. Today it is deemed conservative. Electricity supplied by nuclear power plants has now reached the point where it is cheaper than power produced by burning coal and oil. The most startling proof of this came from a recent decision by the Tennessee Valley Authority to order a two hundred and fifty million dollar atomic power station from the General Electric Company. The 2150-megawatt project is to be built in the heart of the coal country, where the cost of fossil-fuel power is the lowest in the nation. Still, the Tennessee Valley Authority has estimated that its new nuclear plants will be at least eighteen per cent cheaper to operate than a coal-firing plant.

One of the major reasons for choosing nuclear power over fossil-fuel power is that the nuclear plant needs far less space for fuel—one truckload a year, as opposed to the fifty freight-car loads a day needed by the conventional plant. The nuclear plant can use such concentrated fuel by converting energy from matter much more efficiently than does the chemical process of burning.

The difference lies in the structure of the atom. For two thousand years men accepted the Greek idea that the smallest block of matter was the atom, or indivisible particle. We now know that an atom can be divided and its component parts examined. The atom most easily shattered is a form of

The 462,000-kilowatt nuclear generating station in Haddam Neck, Connecticut. Completed in 1967, the plant was built by eleven New England electric utilities who share its generating output. *(Connecticut Yankee Atomic Power Company)*

uranium called U-235. It has within its nucleus ninety-two protons and one hundred and forty-three neutrons—a total of two hundred and thirty-five "nucleons." U-235 is so sensitive that a single neutron flying into it can cause fission. Once a fission process is started, the extra neutrons that are liberated will shatter other uranium atoms causing still more fission. If the process continues, the result is a chain reaction. A runaway chain reaction can lead to an explosion, but if it is controlled, the result can provide vast amounts of power. The basic problem that has slowed the development of atomic power plants has been the scarcity and cost of fuel. U-235, the best fissionable material, is

At the northwest tip of Michigan's lower peninsula the Big Rock Point nuclear plant produces a power output of 75,000 kilowatts, providing electricity to nearly a million customers. *(Consumers Power Company)*

42

rare—less than one per cent of all the uranium found in nature. The main part of it is U-238, a heavy, stable uranium that will not split easily when struck by a flying neutron. But the U-238 is what atomic physicists call a fertile material. Under constant fast-neutron bombardment it can be converted into a readily fissionable substance—plutonium. The fuel that powers a reactor is a combination of fertile and fissionable materials. As the fuel is irradiated, or struck, by neutrons, atoms of the fissionable material are consumed, and, at the same time, the fertile atoms are converted into fissionable fuel. But the percentage of the original fissionable material in the fuel will determine the physical size of the reactor. Thus, most power reactors use an enriched fuel in which the amount of fissionable uranium is about four or five times as much as is normally found in nature. The same effect can be achieved by using another element, thorium, which is converted to U-233 under neutron bombardment. Fissionable uranium U-235 is produced by converting natural uranium to a gas and pumping it through a porous membrane. The lighter U-235 atoms move through a little more quickly, and if the gas is pumped through several thousand membranes, the collection basin at the end will contain a greater percentage of U-235 than is found in nature. The enriched gas is then turned into a solid rod, clad in stainless steel, and sent to the reactor.

Inside the reactor the fissionable U-235 splits and sends its neutrons flying about the fuel core at great speeds. Because slow-moving neutrons can trigger fission more effectively than fast neutrons, a moderator, such as water, is used to slow the neutrons down. The greater the amount of enriched fuel, however, the less need for a moderator. Highly enriched fuels, such as those used in compact reactors, have no moderator at all.

Once the chain reaction has been started, it must be controlled. This is done by controlling the neutron population with substances such as boron and cadmium, which soak up neutrons like a sponge. Like the fuel, they are formed in rods and inserted into the reactor. One set of rods serves as a control to regulate with exact precision the rate of fission by controlling the number of neutrons flying about the core. Another set of rods serves as a safety valve. When inserted into the reactor, they will absorb enough neutrons to halt the fission reaction entirely.

In most power reactors the water moderator serves also as the coolant to protect the reactor core and to pass the heat along, either by itself converting to steam or by producing steam in a secondary loop. The major limiting factor has been the supply and cost of enriched uranium. In the United States the three plants making enriched reactor fuels all tap T.V.A. for their power, and they use great gobs of it—fifty per cent of the Authority's total output. That is equal to five per cent of the total power used in the world, a figure that will increase greatly when the demands of the rest of the world for power begin to approximate our own. To meet the demand, we shall have to develop nuclear plants that create more nuclear fuel than they "burn."

This is not as impossible as it sounds. Breeder reactors, as these modern-day perpetual-motion machines are called, are already being used experimentally. The breeder reactor will use even low-grade sources of U-238 and thorium, both of which exist in plentiful supply. "The consequence

44

of this is so extraordinary," says Dr. Alvin Weinberg, Director of the Oak Ridge National Laboratory, "one will have to describe it as nothing less than the nuclear-energy revolution. If the world uses energy at a rate of some fifty times greater than its present rate, which may happen when we finally develop all the underdeveloped countries, then, in the residual uranium and thorium in the rocks of the earth, we would have enough energy to keep the world going for hundreds of millions of years. We would in effect solve the energy problem forever, permanently for all practical purposes."

Essentially, the breeder reactor is a more elegant furnace than the conventional reactor. It will create three plutonium atoms from the surrounding U-238 for every two atoms of fissionable U-235 used up in the reaction. Experts estimate that over a ten- to fifteen-year period a breeder reactor will produce 1.4 pounds of plutonium from U-238 for every pound of U-235 it burns.

Breeder technology has already moved past the dream and design stages. EBR II, for experimental breeder reactor number II, is already operational and producing sixteen thousand kilowatts of electricity. At full power EBR II can put out twenty megawatts, enough to light and power a city of twenty-five thousand people. But power production is not the primary purpose of the EBR II. Rather, it is a test reactor to determine the feasibility of breeders for central-station power plants. There are problems. The A.E.C. leans toward a sodium-cooled breeder reactor because it makes the breeding process in the case of uranium more efficient. To keep the sodium in a liquid state—an engineering essential—requires very high temperatures. Moreover, it is a tricky and dangerous substance.

If contaminated only slightly by oxygen, it will corrode most metals. If it comes in contact with water, it explodes. Still, the benefits to be gained from the development of an efficient, controllable breeder reactor are enormous, and most estimates are that a large, economical reactor with a reasonable fuel-doubling time will be in service by 1985 at the latest.

If the breeder reactor can be said to excite atomic-power enthusiasts, mention of the fusion reactor makes some of them absolutely rapturous. Fusion is the process that goes on inside the sun. It is at one and the same time the most primal and the most sophisticated of atomic reactions. Under intense heat and pressure hydrogen atoms shed their electrons and are reduced to a nuclear core of a single proton. Within the heart of the sun there occurs what nuclear scientists call the proton-proton reaction, in which protons are fused to form a helium nucleus. The first step in this reaction is the violent collision of two high-energy protons, causing one to lose its charge and fuse as a neutron with the other proton, thus forming a nucleus of deuterium, or heavy hydrogen. The deuterium nuclei fuse with other protons, and then combine to produce helium nuclei.

The thermonuclear-fusion process is well understood by scientists, but it has been mastered only to the extent of building a hydrogen bomb. The chief obstacle to effecting and controlling the fusion reaction, as we do fission, and thus producing enormous amounts of energy, is temperature.

We cannot produce anywhere near the amount of protons that are present in the sun, or exert the gravitational pressures generated by its mass. This pressure drives the protons close enough together for them to overcome the electrical forces of repulsion and allow the nuclear forces of attraction to take over. Under those circumstances, the critical temperature at which fusion is achieved is a mere twenty million degrees. At laboratory pressures fusion cannot take place without the aid of even higher temperatures—on the order of one to two hundred million degrees. To develop such temperatures will require the expenditure of enormous amounts of energy. There is also the problem of containment. At these temperatures, much hotter than the interior of the sun, all is transmuted into a plasma, a hot gas of agitated electrons and primal nucleonic parts such as protons. To maintain such a plasma and to contain it within a reactor is an incredible problem. Walls in the ordinary sense would vaporize in an instant in such temperatures, and so another approach has been to keep the plasma away from the walls by confining it within a "bottle" built from magnetic lines of force. Again, great bursts of energy are required here to build a field of one hundred thousand gauss (the earth itself creates a natural magnetic field of only one gauss). High magnetic fields are unstable, their shapes vary, and their strength is dependent upon the materials that originally created them.

Even if a stable magnetic field is achieved for a long enough period of time, there are still problems. Magnetic fields agitate the plasmas, forcing them into motion that must be compensated for, since fusion cannot take place unless plasmas with a high enough density are contained for at least one tenth second—an event that has thus far not taken place.

At a number of laboratories, however, attempts are being made. At the Lawrence Radiation Laboratory, at Livermore, California, the plasma is pinched into a special shape by a number of magnetic fields. One field is produced by superconducting magnets that step up the force of the field to increase its containment capabilities. Another approach adds accelerated electrons to excite the plasma while it is held within the magnetic bottle.

At Oak Ridge, Tennessee, the Atomic Energy Commission has built the DCX-2, which injects energetic ions—atoms stripped of electrons—into a magnetic bottle at high velocity and then doubles them back on their path. The effect is to force the plasma to build up upon itself. Containment times of two minutes have been achieved by this method, but plasma densities have not been high enough to sustain the fusion reaction.

Princeton University scientists have built a device called the Stellarator, which confines the plasma in an endless ring created by huge magnets circled like a wagon train on the prairie. A stable, dense plasma is the aim of the Princeton research, which uses magnets of varying strengths about the ring to change the field and alter the stability of the plasma.

If fusion ever becomes a technical reality, and there are some scientists who doubt that it is possible, it will be the cheapest, most abundant source of power ever known. Its fuel will be sea water, which is the best source of heavy hydrogen. The nucleus of heavy hydrogen, called deuterium, is the best form of hydrogen for the laboratory fusion reaction. The result will be a reactor that will "burn" the sea and produce enough power to meet the world's energy needs for the rest of time.

Most scientists doubt that fusion reactors will be operating in a practical manner before we are well into the 21st century, but like the proverbial mountain, it offers an immense challenge because we know it is there. Said one nuclear scientist: "The

Model of the nuclear-power generating and desalting plant on a forty-acre man-made island to be built off the coast of Southern California. Two reactors, capable of producing eight hundred megawatts of electricity and fifty million gallons a day of potable water are its planned output. (*Atomic Energy Commission*)

effort to obtain power from fusion is rather like the efforts of the blind men to describe the elephant by exploring its various parts. We are making steady progress in understanding our elephant, but we cannot claim to be able to draw a picture of it: a workable scheme for fusion power. Still, the outline is taking shape. We have little doubt that the beast exists and that the dream of extracting unlimited energy from the seas will one day become a reality."

In any case, the 21st century will unquestionably fall heir to the cheapest and most abundant power supplies in the history of mankind. The leaps of speculative fancy that might be taken at that thought have ranged from the magnificent to the mundane.

Some power-company executives envision a complex of nuclear power generators daily pouring out twelve million kilowatts—enough to supply the 1966 requirements of the entire state of Illinois. At the same time, almost as an afterthought, it could convert over a billion gallons of sea water into fresh every day. The following list, taken from a *Wall Street Journal* article, suggests only a few of the almost limitless uses that could be found for this huge amount of energy. "Electric heating elements embedded in driveways will melt snow the instant it hits, for example. Roadways, including alleys and interstate highways, will be brilliantly lit, cutting accidents and crime. The coldest weather wouldn't stop the home owner from barbecuing on his patio, protected from the elements by curtains of heated air. In factories, automatic machines and materials handling equipment will all but eliminate physical labor, while huge electric-powered lasers or electron beams will cut and shape metal in a fraction of the time now needed."

The application of all this energy might possibly solve the world's food and water needs. Desalinization especially has been an age-old dream that has never been fully realized owing to prohibitive cost. The basic problem has always been energy. To remove the thirty-five hundred parts per million of salt that is in sea water calls for the theoretical expenditure of at least three kilowatt-hours of mechanical work for every thousand gallons of water. At today's prices, a kilowatt-hour of nuclear energy costs approximately one half a cent. By the year 2000 nuclear power may reduce the cost to about a tenth of a cent a kilowatt-hour. That would make the cost of producing a thousand gallons of fresh water less than half a cent. Today, industrial fresh water sells for about twenty cents per thousand gallons, including delivery.

"The trick," explains Dr. Alvin Weinberg, "is to use heat in the form of steam that has gone through a turbine, producing electricity at this very low cost, and then extract the steam from the lower end of the turbine. Before all of its heat has been dissipated, this rather warm steam, perhaps 250 degrees Fahrenheit, is used to boil up sea water. Then, one collects the condensate of the sea water and that is the distilled water."

Even at today's prices, the idea of simultaneously producing electricity and fresh water is far too tantalizing to dismiss. Thus it is that the Metropolitan District in Los Angeles is building a dual-purpose plant that will produce sixteen hundred megawatts of electricity from nuclear-powered reactors and an additional one hundred fifty million gallons of water every day. The price—about thirty cents per thousand gallons—is reasonable.

Eventually, the cost of desalinization may drop to the point where water to irrigate the deserts of

Standing storklike in forty feet of water, this oil and gas platform in the Gulf of Mexico has navigation lights and an electronic foghorn powered by a small nuclear generator. *(Phillips Petroleum Company)*

the world can be extracted from the sea. Indeed, the combination of lower operating costs and the increasing demands of an exploding population will make desalinization for agricultural purposes an absolute necessity.

Economic desalting of water will go a long way toward solving water-pollution problems. The polluted water could be purified in much the same way fresh water is created from sea water, thus yielding still more water for industrial use, irrigation, and human consumption. As a by-product of nuclear power production, water, used over and over again, will be as abundant as man could wish.

Heat will be used not only to desalt water, but also to provide the raw thermal energy that industry needs to make steel, paper, cement, and heavy chemicals. Nuclear-process heat may bring about great economies by providing large quantities of heat without the need for costly transfer systems. With this heat, the steel industry would be able to sever its dependence on coal supplies that are close by. Plants might be set up next to the iron-ore deposits with the ultimate goal of producing in one efficient process a finished product from an input of iron ore. A model and prototype design of such a plant has been prepared by Westinghouse. It would use nuclear energy to melt the ore and nuclear electric energy to turn the rolling mills and run the stamping mill—and some of the heat might possibly be siphoned off to dry the paint on a finished car.

Still another possibility—one that would certainly be a consummation devoutly to be wished—is a junk-free society. Dr. Glenn Seaborg thinks that it could be achieved by the development of huge industrial complexes far from urban areas, controlled by computers and powered by large

51

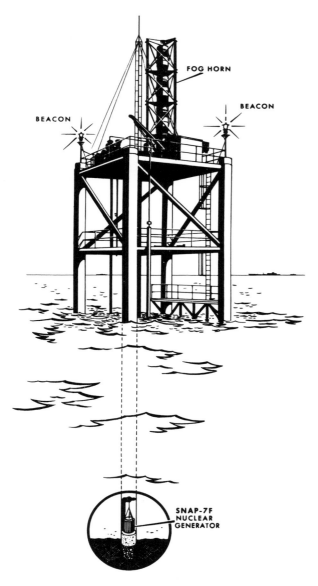

The diagram shows the SNAP-7F generator nested at the bottom of one of the platform's four steel legs. The heat generated from the radioactive decay of the strontium-titanite fuel is converted directly into sixty watts of electricity through the 120 pairs of thermocouples that surround the fuel. *(Martin Company)*

nuclear reactors capable of delivering many million kilowatts of electrical energy.

"Directly associated with and surrounding this energy heart would be a variety of industrial plants, many of which would be interchanging materials and services," Dr. Seaborg explains. "Into one would pour all sorts of scrap from the outside world. This scrap would pass X-ray fluorescence analysis and other automated examinations. On the basis of these, its materials would be broken down, sorted, electrolytically or electromatically separated, and the end products—essentially new, raw materials—routed out to other plants in the complex to be reused. At the same time, these other plants would also be receiving raw materials from other sources. They would be taking in ilmenite, bauxite, and clay and turning out aluminum. They would be using large amounts of hydrocarbons (no longer necessary as fuels) and in huge chlorination works producing solvents, insecticides, and many other materials for industry and agriculture."

From huge complexes to portable generators the size of a bread box, the atom will mean power. The Atomic Energy Commission and private industry have thus far developed more than fifty SNAP (systems for nuclear auxiliary power) generators for a variety of different purposes. Some power floating, unmanned weather stations in the frozen seas of the arctic, others provide the power for satellites orbiting the earth and sending back data. Some SNAPS are powered by radioisotopes—radioactive forms of chemical elements. They are man-made in the heart of a nuclear reactor by the neutron radiation that is one of the by-products of fission. The most powerful of the present radioisotope generators is SNAP-29, a forty-two by thirty-nine-inch book-shaped generator being built by the Martin-Marietta Company for use on the lunar surface and in earth orbital missions. Fueled with polonium-210, the generator will develop five hundred watts of power, about ten times greater than any other SNAP system.

Still, radioisotope power is limited at present, and a great deal of research is aimed at developing SNAP nuclear reactors small enough to be either portable or mobile.

Nuclear reactors have been going to sea with remarkable efficiency for the past decade. Today, the commissioning of a nuclear-propelled warship in the United States scarcely rates a line on the back page of the newspaper, so commonplace has the act become. There are now seventy-four vessels with nuclear power plants for propulsion and auxiliary electrical power in the United States Navy. Merchant ships, too, will become a nuclear commonplace in the 21st century. The first of the line, the *Savannah*, although dogged by controversy and politics, showed that nuclear power was feasible for civilian as well as military vessels.

Nuclear prophets such as Dr. Bernard Spinrad of the Argonne National Laboratory foresee compact reactors eventually powering airplanes, huge passenger-carrying dirigibles, and possibly trains. Francis Morse of Boston University is another dreamer who foresees a nuclear-powered dirigible as large as an ocean liner, cruising the world, never landing, but boarding and disembarking passengers from a small ferry plane that would land and take off from a small hangar amidships. With the exception of NERVA, the A.E.C. has refused to fund work on airborne reactors, but there seems no limit to the uses on earth and in space of SNAP devices, for which the A.E.C. has a large program.

Perhaps the least exploited form of potentially

An artist's concept of an underwater navigational and research station to be powered by a SNAP-21 generator. This generator, fueled by strontium-90, is designed for deep-sea use by packaging in a lightweight corrosion-resistant vessel capable of withstanding underwater pressures up to 10,000 pounds per square inch. *(Minnesota Mining and Manufacturing Company)*

53

useful nuclear energy is the original source of its great research impetus—the explosive power of the bomb itself. The reluctance to use a nuclear explosion for peaceful purposes can be ascribed primarily to the fear of proliferation of nuclear weapons. At the moment the nuclear club is sharply limited. The United States, the Soviet Union, France, Great Britain, and China are the only bomb-carrying members. The economics of A-bomb and H-bomb building as well as political considerations deter most of the other industrially advanced nations from developing their own nuclear weapons. Treaties banning atmospheric testing and the spread of nuclear weapons to nonnuclear nations have been signed, but not by all members of the club. Nevertheless, the bomb is very much in our thoughts—so much so it has colored much of our thinking. Thus, an ambitious project designed to use the explosive power of the bomb for peaceful purposes—to dig canals, harbors, dams, underground reservoirs, and mountain passes—has been bedeviled by fear of the bomb. This has been the fate thus far of Project Plowshare, but there are signs that it may yet use a nuclear explosion for peaceful ends. Recently, it set off the first commercially sponsored nuclear blast in history. A twenty-foot-long nuclear device carrying the energy of twenty-six thousand tons of TNT was placed four thousand feet beneath a pine-studded mesa in northern New Mexico. The blast ripped open layers of the stony underworld that sealed in rich deposits of natural gas. It will take about two years to complete all of the tests after the blast and determine whether it was successful. The hope is that nuclear blasts such as this will make accessible the natural gas now sealed up under thirty thousand square miles of formations that stretch from New

SNAP generators are ideal power sources for remote areas, whether underwater or in outer space. The Nimbus-B weather spacecraft, seen undergoing tests in an anechoic chamber, will carry two SNAP-19 generators to power day and night cameras and sensors for atmospheric measurements on a global basis. *(General Electric Company)*

This experimental satellite carries a SNAP-3 generator, shown here as the white baseball-sized bull's-eye at the center of the satellite's base. *(Martin Company)*

The flanged device in the center of this drawing is an atomic power plant on the moon. Already in the design stages, the reactor will power an instrument package that will be left on the moon by the Apollo astronauts. The information obtained by the instruments will be sent to earth by the telemetry antenna to the right of the atomic power plant. *(General Electric Company)*

Mexico to Canada. Using conventional methods, engineers could hope to produce about five hundred million cubic feet of gas in twenty years—about ten per cent of the gas in the formation—from the blast site. The nuclear blast, however, is expected to increase that yield by sevenfold—to three and a half million cubic feet or seventy per cent of the gas in the formation.

"If Gasbuggy succeeds," declares Nobel Laureate and former U.S. Atomic Energy Commissioner Willard S. Libby, "we will have the immediate problem of supplying enough Plowshare devices to keep on with it. Its success might also change the attitudes of Britain, Canada, France, and other countries toward Plowshare. . . . Plowshare's closeness to bombs has caused people to worry, but the prospects are hopeful. Reasonable people will eventually prevail. After all, I'm told gunpowder was applied for six centuries before it was used for peaceful purposes."

One of the first peaceful uses of the bomb may be to dig another Panama Canal. The U.S. Army Corps of Engineers will shortly present a plan to Congress to blast a new sea-level canal across Central America. Called the Isthmian Canal, the huge ditch would be dug with more than five hundred atomic devices, at less than half the cost of conventional methods. The time needed for the excavation would also be reduced sharply, from ten, to three or four years.

Other even more visionary but not impossible dreams include the application of an atomic bomb's heat and pressure to foster chemical reactions. Among the most notable of these would be the manufacture of diamonds from graphite, a feat already accomplished with dynamite by the Stanford Research Institute.

"If dynamite can do it," adds Dr. Libby, "nuclear explosions can do it better. Maybe we could make a ton of diamonds at once."

The ultimate potential of the atom is incalculable. If energy is the only true wealth, the 21st century should produce a civilization that can banish all want and care from the face of the earth. The idea of nuclear energy has dazzled man for much of this century. As early as 1914 H. G. Wells predicted the development of nuclear energy. He foresaw the bomb and then the use of the atom to develop cheap power. The result, he felt, would be that nuclear energy would set the world free. In 1967 Dr. Alvin Weinberg, Director of the Oak Ridge National Laboratory, said: "Many of us in the nuclear-energy business have always joked a little about H. G. Wells' 1914 vision. And yet, in the past two years, there have been such remarkable advances in the technique of producing nuclear energy that we have suddenly had to come to grips with the possibility that nuclear energy will, in fact, set the world free."

In the 21st century it is also to be hoped that the world will know how to make use of this freedom.

This crater in the Nevada desert, 320 feet deep and 1200 feet in diameter, was formed in an instant by a 100-kiloton thermonuclear device to demonstrate the earth-moving potential of the atom. In this test, the single device moved 7.5 million cubic yards of earth in a single explosion. *(Lawrence Radiation Laboratory, Livermore)*

3

The Laser–
The Light Fantastic

In his exploration of the cosmos, of the earth and the sea around him, in the laboratory and in the operating room, the scientist of tomorrow will use a tool so ubiquitous, so versatile, that it may be dubbed the Scotch tape of the 21st century. The tool is the laser, a device capable of delivering an intense beam of energy over long distances with almost no dispersion or loss of power. The first working laser was put together in 1960, and the applications that have been found for it already number in the hundreds. But, amazingly, the first intimation of such a device appeared in 1897, when H. G. Wells published *The War of the Worlds*. Wells described a Martian invasion of the earth. "The invasion was backed by an immensely powerful weapon—a mysterious sword of heat. This intense heat they project in a parallel beam against any object they choose by means of a polished parabolic mirror of unknown composition, much as the parabolic mirror of a lighthouse projects a beam of light. . . . Whatever is combustible flashes into flame at its touch, lead runs like water, it softens iron, cracks and melts glass and when it falls upon water, incontinently that explodes into steam."

Incredibly, Wells seemed to be describing the modern-day laser. The enormous energies it produces can not only turn lead liquid but when focused to a narrow beam at close range can instantly vaporize any substance on earth—*poof*—like that.

As a death ray, the laser today has all the punch of a popgun, but its constructive uses are already staggering. The laser is used to mill steel by melting the top few thousandths of an inch and detect art frauds, to erase tattoos and weld detached retinas, to make three-dimensional photographs and transmit television pictures. And this is only the beginning. One day it may drill tunnels, illuminate the black depths of the ocean, carry millions of electronic messages, detect earthquakes, and prevent tooth decay.

Yet despite the tremendous excitement, the eager rush to uncover still newer and more fanciful applications for the laser, it has already fallen victim to the awful judgment of premature expectation. The surge of speculation, bordering at times on the fanciful, and even on the magical, began in 1958 when the principle of the laser was first elucidated in a paper by Charles H. Townes, now at the University of California, and his brother-in-law, Arthur Schawlow, now head of the physics department at Stanford University. Townes and Schawlow discussed the feasibility of amplifying light. Their paper was the outcome of previous research in the United States in the early 1950s. Scientists had found that certain gas molecules could be made to oscillate in a fixed pattern. The oscillations were set in motion by exciting the gas with a jolt of high-frequency electricity. The shape of the molecules determined the frequency of vibration. So regular were the frequencies that they could be counted like the measured beat of a metronome and thus became the new time standard in the United States.

Charles Townes, then at Columbia University, seized upon the idea and worried it the way a dog gnaws a bone. It should be possible, he reasoned, to make a gas such as ammonia do far more than serve as a frequency standard. It might even be possible to use the ammonia molecules to amplify a signal and produce microwave frequencies of remarkable purity. By 1954 Townes and two co-workers had succeeded in building an apparatus that agitated ammonia molecules to the point where they produced a steady stream of microwaves. The device was named maser, after its principle, microwave amplification by stimulated emission of radiation.

The maser was swiftly put to work. Radio astronomers used it as a means of amplifying the faint radio signals from galaxies billions of light years away. Closer to home, the maser became the microwave amplifier for the first communications satellites.

The maser was a handy device. What might happen if the frequencies used by the maser could be kicked upstairs, into the next higher register of the electromagnetic spectrum—light? Townes and his brother-in-law, Arthur Schawlow, who was then at Bell Laboratories, wrote the famous paper describing that possibility. They even suggested two systems for achieving the result, but neither seemed to work. Nor did the name they gave this new principle—optical maser. The principle was one of light amplification by stimulated emission of radiation, or laser, and that is the name that stuck.

It fell to Theodore H. Maiman, then a physicist at the Hughes Research Laboratory, to develop the first working laser device. Maiman used a cylindrical rod of synthetic ruby, which chemically is an aluminum-oxide crystal containing a trace of chromium, an impurity that gives the gem its red color. The ideal arrangement for the laser, Maiman discovered, is five chromium atoms for every two thousand aluminum atoms. Maiman then ground both ends of the rod flat and silvered one end, making it a mirror to reflect all the light rays striking it. The other end of the rod was short-changed. It was half silvered, enough to bounce back the light striking it for a time, but when sufficient light energy had been accumulated by pumping atoms from a low- to a high-energy state, it would burst through the half-silvered end.

The next step was to wind a long tubular photo-flash in a tight spiral around the ruby rod and hook it up to a timer that would regulate the frequency of the flashes. Each flash of the tube excited the chromium atoms in the ruby, jolting their electrons from their familiar orbits about the nucleus and into higher energy levels. The effect is only temporary, and the agitated electrons drop back into their original orbit when stimulated by the incoming signal of the proper frequency. But in the process, each electron gives off a photon, a quantum of light energy that serves as the basic unit of light. The majority of these photons are ping-ponged between the two mirrors at each end of the rod. The rushing photons trigger other excited electrons to give off still more packets of light energy until a furious mob of photons hurtles between the mirrors, back and forth, again and again, millions of times.

Since the photons are dashing back and forth at the same frequency, they are all the same color—red—and eventually the red light begins to leak through the half-silvered mirror. Then, in a sudden burst of tremendous energy, the bulk of the photons erupt in one mighty surge of radiation from the "half" mirror at the end of the ruby rod. The process, from beginning to end, takes only a few thousandths of a second, and the laser pulse itself may last for less than ten millionths of a second. But in that flick of time, the laser can punch through a steel blade with a light that is a million times purer, more concentrated, and more powerful than any light known in nature.

A ruby laser is used to blast a 0.02-inch-diameter crater
in a sheet of stainless steel. The laser beam develops a
temperature of 4800 degrees Fahrenheit, instantly
vaporizing the point where it strikes the steel.

The tremendous energies and the myriad uses of the laser all stem from the fact that laser light is coherent. Although light energy has been quantified and described as a particle—the photon—all light travels in waves similar to the ripples moving across a pond. The number of waves that pass a specific point every second determines the frequency of that light. The distance between the top, or crest, of one wave to the crest of the one behind it is called the wave length and determines the color of the light wave. The light that illuminates our homes and offices, the white light produced by an incandescent bulb, is composed of a jumble of different frequencies traveling in all directions. Such white light, actually the product of many colors, or frequencies, is called incoherent light. By contrast, laser light is coherent. It is exclusively composed of one wave length, or color, with each wave moving in the same direction and in phase, so that the crests all reinforce one another. Like an army drill team, the waves of coherent light are precisely in step with each other, thus producing an extremely straight, narrow beam over long distances. Incoherent light, say that coming from a flashlight, will fan out over a wide area, and the farther it is projected, the wider the area will be.

A few years ago a small ruby laser fired a series of pulses at the moon, almost a quarter of a million miles away. The laser beam lighted the lunar surface with a circle less than two miles in diameter. Were it possible to send a beam from a searchlight across the same distance, it would, when it struck the moon, fan out to the point of being several times the moon's 2160-mile diameter.

Ruby lasers are called pulse lasers because they produce bursts of light. They have also been called

In this photograph of the earth, seen as a crescent by a Surveyor 7 television camera on the moon, the arrow shows the two sites on the dark side of the earth from which laser beams were aimed at the moon. The beams were photographed and relayed back to earth on January 20, 1968. *(NASA)*

The world's smallest laser is a semiconductor type, made of one square millimeter of gallium arsenide, seen at right. Mounted on a transistor-type header, as shown on the penny, it is used in communications devices and in computers.

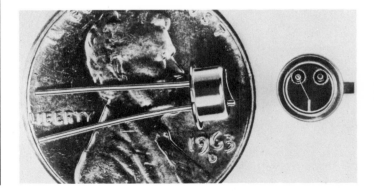

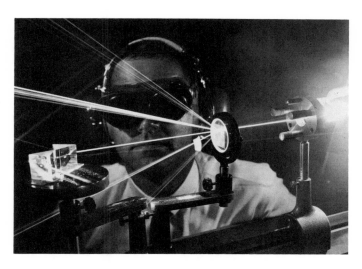

This argon-gas laser can generate up to eight watts of power at several different wave lengths within the blue-green region of the visible spectrum. *(Hughes Aircraft)*

Another form of gas laser is this helium-neon device operated at the Oak Ridge National Laboratory. Its beam is a single wave length red light with a power of about five watts. *(Oak Ridge National Laboratory)*

solid-state lasers, an acknowledgment of the crystal state of matter to which the ruby belongs. A second form of laser, the gas laser, looks much like a neon tube, but instead of emitting its laser light in pulses it gives off what amounts to a continuous beam of energy. The third type of laser also emits its energy in a continuous wave. Called an injection or semiconductor laser, it produces its energy at the junction between two types of impurities in a semiconductor crystal such as gallium arsenide. Despite the differences in technique and output, the three types of laser all conform to the same basic principle that Schawlow and Townes first set down in 1958.

Once the technology of laser construction had been fairly well developed by Maiman and the others who followed, the inevitable reaction set in. When so few of the way-out predictions for the laser were immediately achieved, the clichés were applied. The laser was described as an invention in search of a job, a solution looking for a problem. Such descriptions were sheer nonsense, the product of the "breakthrough" mania that insists that every new technological and scientific advance cure cancer, fly thousands of people thousands of miles in minutes, or just be a "bold new advance."

The simple fact is the laser must be applied to specific tasks, perhaps even to tasks that do not yet exist, on the simple basis of whether it will do the job and do it better than anything else.

"In some ways," says Arthur Schawlow, "I can't help thinking that the laser is not very much ahead of where the airplane was around 1910; it would fly, but if you talked of crossing the ocean with a hundred passengers at the speed of sound, people would think you were crazy. And you couldn't have done it, no matter what you spent.

You had to develop the whole science of aerodynamics, get rid of the wood and cloth and develop light-weight metals, and you had to have real inventions, like the jet engine. Once you got off the ground, the rest of it had to come. So, we'll have these high-power, high-energy lasers, maybe sooner than we think, and they'll be cheap too, in time. Now what we'll do with them, I think will require some more ingenuity. But some of the obvious things we know."

Among the more obvious laboratory tricks was the ability of the laser to punch a hole in a razor blade when the intense beam of light struck it and was converted into intense heat. Although there wasn't much demand for such a showy but non-utilitarian effect, there was a need for holes to be punched in diamonds. The Western Electric Company wears out thousands of diamond dies in the process of producing thirty million miles of thin wire for telephones each year. The wire is brought down to its gossamer gauge by drawing it through a hole in a diamond.

Diamonds are the world's hardest substances, and drilling through them was a tedious two-day affair using steel pins coated with olive oil and diamond dust. Now the job is done in a few minutes. A ruby-laser beam hammers at the diamond until a hole of precisely the right size is made. Since diamond and hole are extremely small, they are magnified eighty times and projected on a television screen. The laser operator watches the results on the screen, penetrating the diamond with focused laser bursts that are precisely regulated to avoid shattering it.

Heat has been the key to many laser applications. One of the most dramatic is the complete vaporization of any substance.

Arthur Schawlow, chairman of the physics department at Stanford University and coinventor of the maser, demonstrates a laser eraser. The device generates just enough heat to vaporize the black letters off a typewritten page, leaving the white paper intact, since it reflects the laser light instead of absorbing it.

"The point is that the laser does vaporize a small bit of material and vaporizes it very completely," explains Schawlow. "Not just a part of it. The whole thing is blasted right off and you get a true sample of a very tiny part of the specimen. In this manner, you can study, for example, the transport of metals across the membranes of dividing cells. This ability of the laser to focus on a very tiny spot is being used in other parts of biology. You can irradiate a part of a cell, for example, destroy the nucleus of a cell, without damaging the walls. Or drill a hole in a cell—I've seen a hole drilled in a little red blood corpuscle—though just why you want a hole in a red blood corpuscle I don't know, but you can do it!"

Scientists such as Dr. David Glick, of the Stanford University Medical Center in California, are finding ways to use the enormous power of the laser to identify biological materials. Focusing the beam through a microscope (the hybrid device is called a microprobe) on a dot of tissue just two hundredths of an inch in diameter, he blasts away with a ten billionth of a second pulse that generates a temperature of eighteen thousand degrees. The "zap" vaporizes an infinitesimal amount of tissue—as little as one millionth of an ounce—and leaves only a microscopic pinhole in the zapped tissue.

The vaporized material is heat-boosted by an electric spark, which sends it streaming upward past a spectrograph. The spectrograph is an all-purpose device used to identify virtually any substance by analyzing the light waves it gives off. Every element emits electromagnetic waves of a certain length. If the wave length is present, the element can most certainly be identified as being present.

With the microprobe and the spectrograph, Glick

At the University of Cincinnati's Medical Center a laser scalpel is used to remove the pigmented skin that forms a tattoo on the arm of a patient.

has found calcium, iron, cobalt, and zinc, as well as other elements, in adrenal glands, kidneys, and teeth. Direct analysis of skin, teeth, and hair have been obtained by zapping laboratory animals and human volunteers with no harmful effects.

This, however, does not mean that the laser is completely innocuous. The fabled death ray is a technical possibility, although still, fortunately, somewhat remote.

A symposium called by the American Association for the Advancement of Science reported that some of the more powerful lasers already in use in a variety of fields were capable of causing serious eye damage to people who are struck by the invisible beam of light, even though those people are more than a mile and a half away; blinding similar persons at distances of a mile or less; and literally blowing a man's eye out of his head at distances under fifty yards. One member of the panel described the following experiment: "When laser beams were directed at the forehead of mice from a distance of five or six inches . . . with a one centimeter spot size, there was only slight damage at the surface of the forehead.

"Examination of the interior of the skull, however, revealed hemorrhage throughout the brain, in the cerebrospinal fluids as well as within the substance of the brain.

"The mice either died immediately or experienced serious neurological effects. When glass was interposed between the beam and the animal, the damage was increased."

The researchers also focused the laser beam on the backs of mice and "produced extensive skin damage and mild temporary paralysis. Permanent paralysis or death resulted when higher energy densities were used."

Dr. Edmund Klein, Chief of Dermatology at the Roswell Park Memorial Institute, in Buffalo, New York, one of the world's great cancer-research centers, dashed a lot of early hopes for the laser as a sort of superscalpel in cancer surgery. "Living tumor cells, when struck by the laser beam," noted Dr. Klein, "might just as easily be pushed into deeper tissue or even into the blood or lymph circulations, causing the tumor to spread faster."

As for infectious diseases, some studies have shown that there are forms of hardy bacteria that can survive the blistering impact of the laser beam and in the process may be shoved through the skin or deeper into tissues, where they can set up pockets of infection.

However, these dangers can be avoided by the exercise of common sense and caution. The role of the laser as a healing agent seems to be growing at a pace similar to its new-found uses in other fields.

One of the pioneers in examining this new field of laser surgery is Dr. Leon Goldman, of the University of Cincinnati. At the University's Medical Center, Dr. Goldman has the world's first laser operating suite. In it he treats such medical problems as tattoo removal and precancerous skin tumors.

In both cases the technique is the same. The laser is tuned to a specific frequency so that the beam will be absorbed by the darker colors and reflected by the lighter ones. Tattoos are removed by burning the skin colored by the tattoo. The lighter-colored surrounding skin reflects the laser light, thus preventing the energy from being converted into heat. Where the light is absorbed on the tattoo, the sensation is somewhat akin to being burned by a drop of hot candle wax.

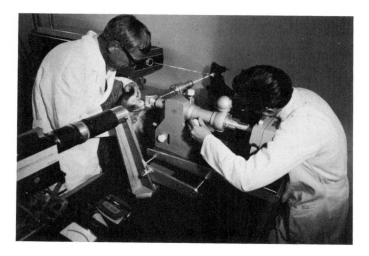

As a medical tool, the laser has found one of its most important uses in eye surgery. Here, it is used first to tear and then to repair the retinal tissue in a monkey's eye.

Most of the human eye diseases now treated with the laser are those which afflict the retina, the light-sensitive tissue layer of the eye. In some cases the retina becomes detached from another layer of tissue called the choroid. With a small, hand-held laser, the surgeon can produce a tiny scar that will tack the retina back down and restore vision to the patient.

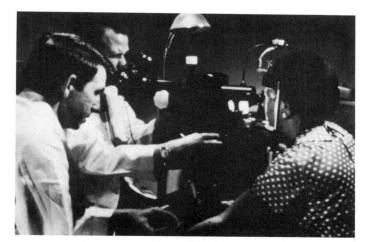

In the far more pressing area of treating cancer, the laser has limited, though promising, effectiveness. Skin cancers and precancerous tumors of the skin are often dark colored—hence the name melanoma—or they can be artificially colored to absorb the laser's light and convert it to heat. The searing beam destroys potentially malignant tissue swiftly and bloodlessly, its enormous heat sealing severed blood vessels before the blood can spill through the wound. The procedure is still experimental, owing to the danger of blasting cancer cells deeper into the skin. A bloodless light-knife, a laser scalpel that will cauterize the incision the instant it is made, may be the laser's greatest contribution to 21st-century surgery.

It has already found a rather important niche in the 20th-century practice of ophthalmology. A number of diseases of the retina, the thin membrane that receives the image formed by the lens of the eye, are now repaired by the laser beam. A common disease that can lead to blindness is the detachment of the light-sensitive retina from another layer of tissue called the choroid.

Treatment of these detachments of the retina and other similar problems have in the past been done with a so-called photocoagulator, which uses visible light from a xenon arc to scar the retina at the point of detachment and thus seal it down. But the photocoagulator is bulky and must remain fixed in position when it is in use. Also, it produces large scars that reduce the amount of retinal tissue available for the image. The laser, by contrast, is hand-held and can be focused down to a pinpoint, producing a tiny scar that tacks down the retina just as securely as the much larger scars made by the photocoagulator.

Eventually, the laser might be adapted to treat

A number of eye diseases might one day be treated by the laser. In research on animals, attempts have been made to burn through cataracts which cloud the lens of the eye and also to treat glaucoma by burning through the blocks that impede the flow of blood to the eye, producing tremendous pressure and pain inside the eye.

68

other forms of eye disease, such as tumors, and the eye complications produced by diabetes. Some ophthalmologists foresee the laser burning holes in the iris of the eye to restore vision. The iris, which controls the size of the pupil, thus determining the amount of light that enters the eye, can be closed or seriously deformed by disease. Still another disease, glaucoma, a major cause of blindness in the United States, might be treated with the laser. Glaucoma produces tremendous amounts of pressure inside the eye by blocking the blood that enters it. A laser could destroy the tissue that blocks the outflow of blood and possibly preserve vision for the glaucoma victim.

From medicine to industry, to physics, to space, to communications, the increasing uses to which the laser is being put are mounting with dizzying rapidity. The microprobe laser is an example. First developed in the biomedical laboratory, it is finding an array of uses not only in these fields but also in industry. One of the most remarkable of these is its use in authenticating art treasures. Frederick Brech, of the Jarrell-Ash Company in Waltham, Massachusetts, who developed many industrial uses for the microprobe, has become a sort of art detective. Brech collaborates with William J. Young, scientific curator of the Boston Museum of Fine Arts, to confirm the age, source, and authenticity of rare objects. A case in question was a small portrait attributed to a sixteenth-century artist known as Le Maître de Bruges. Young doubted its authenticity because X-rays passed through it too easily. Had the painting been authentic, they would have been blocked by the lead carbonate that was used in 16th-century pigments.

The painting was put under the microprobe and "zapped." The resulting spectrogram revealed the

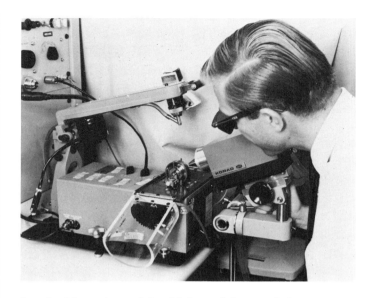

A pulsed laser is used for high-precision work in balancing gyroscope wheels.

The laser and the microscope combine to weld miniature electronic circuits.

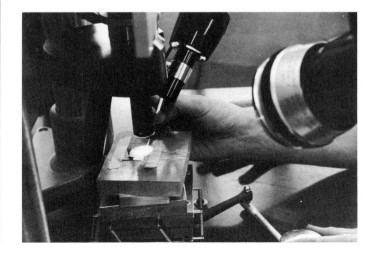

presence of zinc, certain evidence that the portrait was a fraud. Zinc-based pigments were not used until 1820.

Heat—intense, concentrated heat—is the means by which the laser can vaporize materials. At the Korad Corporation, in Santa Monica, California, this heat is used to balance the rings of gyroscopes. Instead of the tedious machine-milling techniques formerly used, laser pulses lasting a mere fifty millionths of a second create temperatures of three thousand degrees Fahrenheit on the rough edges of the ring. The burrs and bulges of the metal are vaporized away, thus balancing the ring more accurately than any other method known.

Welding is another job that the heat of the laser beam can do remarkably well. The microcircuits of delicate electronic parts so small they must be viewed under a microscope are now welded by laser. The process takes three thousandths of a second, as a laser welder beams five thousand degrees Fahrenheit, onto a surface smaller than the diameter of a human hair. The weld is perfect, as the chemical impurities in the metal are vaporized before they can contaminate the joint.

In some microcircuits cross-hair accuracy is essential, for welds must be made at a given point, without affecting ultrasensitive materials adjacent to the joint. Gold wires in some circuits are welded by bursts of a thousand degrees while the temperatures of circuits a hair's breadth away remain unaffected.

Heat is not the only asset in the laser's bag of electromagnetic tricks. The remarkable coherency first demonstrated by those regimented ammonia molecules oscillating in such precise step, which first started Townes thinking about the possibilities of coherence and precision of frequency, are pres-

This is the technician's microview of the wires and circuits he must weld with the laser.

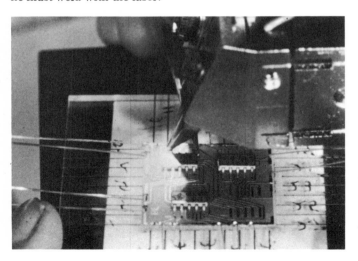

So straight is the laser beam, it is being used to align the San Francisco-Oakland Bay Tunnel, now under construction. Laser transits such as this keep the dredges exactly on course.

ent in remarkable abundance in the laser. As a straight edge, the laser is probably unequalled in all of technology, and in nature, too, for that matter. And this fact has not escaped notice. Oakland and San Francisco's multibillion-dollar transportation adventure, BART, Bay Area Rapid Transit Project, uses a covey of specially adapted laser transits to keep a fleet of dredging tugs on station in the bay. The vessels are part of an ambitious project to dig a trench twenty thousand feet long across the Bay to connect San Francisco and Oakland by tunnel. A specially constructed tube will eventually be laid in the trench to carry commuters on rapid-transit facilities across the Bay.

In New Mexico an irrigation-tunnel drilling operation was kept on target by a laser system. The accuracy of the laser becomes even more important to the physicist who uses its sharp, unwavering beam to align precisely the devices he builds. One of the newest is the two-mile-long linear accelerator recently completed at Stanford University. This accelerator is in essence a two-mile tube through which high-speed electrons can be fired at atomic targets. The target materials are smashed, and the debris is studied by physicists. The design did not permit the accelerator to be out of line more than half a millimeter over its entire two-mile length. The conventional means of alignment—stretched wires or ordinary lights—were simply not precise enough.

This was a job for superlight, the laser, which enabled the builders to detect misalignments of as little as 0.025 of a millimeter at any of the two hundred and seventy-four alignment stations on the accelerator's path.

Still another dazzlingly efficient function of the laser is its ability to measure distances. As a range finder the laser makes radar look clumsy by comparison. But like radar, laser range finders operate on the principle of sending out a pulse of electromagnetic waves and then measuring the time it takes them to reach their target and return. At a range of five hundred miles radar can establish distance within an error of one hundred feet; the laser reduces the error to twenty-five feet. In tracking satellites, laser range finders can measure distances one hundred miles out in space to within thirty-six inches.

One of the most fascinating adaptations of the range finder is the laser altimeter. In one demonstration an airplane carrying the laser altimeter flew over a football field at an altitude of one thousand feet and a speed of two hundred and fifty miles an hour. Astonishingly, the laser registered the fact that the cross bars on the goal posts were not quite at regulation height. It also noted that the pitch of the bars was not quite in accordance with regulations.

Such accuracy is obviously not needed in aircraft, but it can be used in the laboratory and in the machine shop, where ultraprecise tolerances must be achieved. An instrument called the laser interferometer, which compares the interference patterns between two continuous laser beams, can provide incredibly accurate measurements—length changes as small as one hundred billionth of an inch are possible.

The laser generates light, and light is the essential ingredient in photography. It is not surprising, therefore, to see one of the earliest and most startling uses of the laser being made in the field of photography. But there is an otherworldly quality to the story, a quality that in times past would have been described as fictional, or serendipitous,

This two-mile-long building houses the Stanford University Linear Accelerator, the world's longest "atom smasher," which produces a beam of electrons at twenty billion electron volts for research into the heart of matter.

Its main component is a straight-line track, or wave guide, in 240 sections. Mounted on adjustable jacks, a laser beam is focused through long sections of the accelerator.

The interference patterns from the split laser beams look like a series of gray smudges on the hologram, which contains all the information necessary to reconstruct a three-dimensional picture when viewed by laser light. *(Bell Telephone Laboratories)*

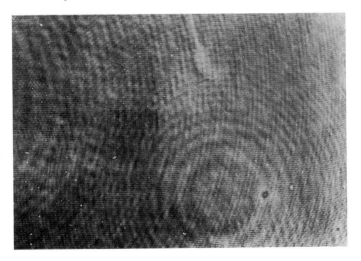

but which with our present preoccupation with the future must be considered proleptic—a sort of dramatic fragment of the 21st century played out for our edification here and now. The story begins with a Hungarian-British physicist named Denis Gabor. In 1948 Gabor published a paper describing a photographic system whereby three-dimensional pictures could be produced without using a camera, a lens, or a shutter. But three-dimensional lensless photography was merely a principle that had been elucidated. It didn't even have a name. That was supplied years later, in 1964, by George Stroke, an engineer at the University of Michigan. He called it holography. It is today used for a variety of purposes, none of which Gabor had in mind. "I wanted to improve the electron microscope," Gabor explains. "I wanted to see atoms with the electron microscope, and maybe it will be used some day for that. But after about three years of work, there was absolutely no echo of this until the laser was invented and then, at once, holography exploded."

It is estimated that some five hundred industrial and university laboratories are now involved in holography research and development in the United States alone.

A laser beam is split into two beams, one of which illuminates the subject, and the light reflected from it falls on a photographic plate. The second beam is aimed at a mirror, bounces off it, and also strikes the plate. Where the two beams meet, on the plate, they produce a pattern of alternating dark and bright lines known as interference fringes. To the naked eye, the plate seems covered with gray smudges. Despite its disappointing appearance, it carries the impressive name of hologram. The hologram becomes impressive only

By splitting a laser beam so that one half shines on an object and then is reflected onto a photographic plate and the other half strikes the plate directly, a pattern will be etched into the emulsion. If a laser light is then beamed through the plate, a three-dimensional image can be seen. This is holography, or lenseless three-dimensional photography.

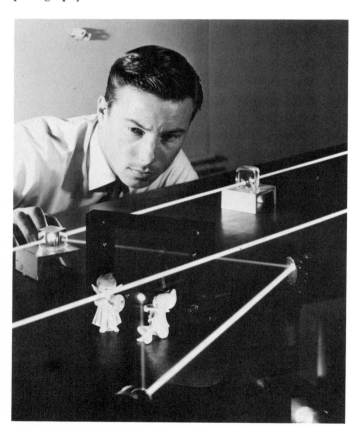

when a laser beam shines through it. Then, as if a curtain had suddenly been parted, the plate becomes a window, framing a three-dimensional image of the object originally "photographed" by the laser beams. Altering the basic technique, the use of different-colored laser beams allows the hologram to be rendered in full color.

"In the hologram," explains George Stroke, "the light waves are stored in a manner similar to the way a musical tone is stored in a piano string. It is there, but it is not released until the string is plucked."

To what uses shall we put the hologram in the 21st century? Speculation has already run the gamut from three-dimensional full-color television to holograms hung on the wall as if they were three-dimensional paintings. Of immense importance will be the harnessing of holography to microscopy, enabling scientists to photograph microorganisms in three-dimensional color, rather than the flat two-dimensional view they are now offered. And perhaps even Gabor's original idea of enhancing the electron microscope will be realized.

Gabor had to wait sixteen years for the laser to make his idea a reality. Alexander Graham Bell, the inventor of the telephone, might have achieved still another monumental communications breakthrough had the laser been available to him. In 1880 he invented the photophone, a device that transmitted sound over ordinary light waves. The photophone used a vibrating mirror to modulate a beam of sunlight and then converted the vibrations to sound. "I have heard a ray of the sun laugh and cough and sing," wrote Bell after the first successful demonstration of his photophone. But despite Bell's poetic enthusiasm, radio waves and electric wires turned out to be more efficient carriers of messages.

The individual frequencies that carry electronic communications can be classed as bands of varying widths. The higher the frequencies within a band, the greater its information-carrying capabilities. Similarly, the higher frequencies carry more information in the same period of time. As a corollary, the more information you wish carried, the more frequencies you need. In other words, to pack more information into the air, the widest band widths are required. Thus a single television station will use a band of frequencies six million cycles wide to carry all of the information needed to transmit picture and sound signals to a television receiver. One television station uses up six times the space needed by all of the one hundred and seven AM radio stations for their broadcast signals. But, if it were possible to go from the radio-wave spectrum up into the next higher band—visible light—the range of frequencies would provide room for ten million television channels. The coherent beam of light produced by the laser has the information-carrying capability to haul all of the information we now send by radio, television, telephone, telegraph, and satellite. One estimate has it that half of the population of the world could talk simultaneously to the other half on one laser beam.

We have not achieved such a capability yet, but the laser has carried television pictures and voice communications experimentally. There are many problems that stand in the way of the laser as a communications carrier, not the least of which is the fact that the laser beam is, after all, only a beam of light. Hence, even atmospheric disturb-

This multiple exposure photograph is an attempt to show how a viewer can literally see around the corners of an object in a hologram. The graininess of the photo is characteristic of an object illuminated by laser light. *(Bell Telephone Laboratories)*

This laser, seen at lower left, carries a television picture with the aid of a modulator—the black cylinder mounted in the path of the laser beam. The modulator takes the electrical signals coming from the TV camera at a rate of four million per second and places them on a laser beam. A detector at the end of the laser device receives the modulated beam and converts it back into the electrical pulsations that form the picture on the television screen. *(Westinghouse)*

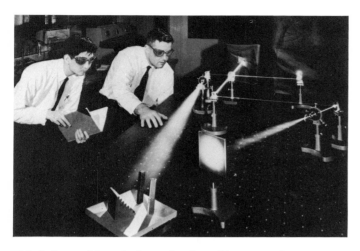

This holographic technique, developed by researchers at Bell Telephone Laboratories and the University of Michigan, first combines two laser beams of different colors into a single beam and then splits them to produce a multicolor hologram. A multicolor, three-dimensional image is obtained when the hologram is illuminated by the laser beam. *(Bell Telephone Laboratories)*

This multicolor hologram can also be viewed by shining ordinary white light—either sunlight or a flashlight beam—on it.

ances would disrupt its transmission. Even beaming to satellites for retransmission does not solve the problem, because such ephemeral interference problems as clouds, heavy fog, rain, or snow are enough to scatter the beam. A possible solution now being considered is the use of wave guides, which are pipes made of glass or other materials.

Where the laser may truly perform a communications service is in deep space, where man is unquestionably headed. Serious doubts have already been established as to the ability of radio-wave systems to carry information rapidly enough through the enormous distances involved in interplanetary travel. The voyage of Mariner IV, which resulted in historic pictures being sent back to earth from within a few thousand miles of the Martian surface, demonstrated the limitations of radio frequencies for space communications. The radio waves were only able to carry eight and one third information "bits" every second. This meant that each picture required more than eight hours to form. The same picture sent on a laser beam could have been formed one million times faster.

The need to carry great information loads to and from space will be a major one in the 21st century. For space will be one of our major targets for exploration, and the laser will surely be one of the major tools used to accomplish that purpose.

Part Two:
The Targets of Tomorrow

To see a World in a Grain of Sand,
And a Heaven in a Wild Flower,
Hold Infinity in the palm of your hand,
And Eternity in an hour.

—WIILLIAM BLAKE

4

To the Moon

From man's earliest days the moon has been the queen of his heavens. But until the spectacular success of the American and Russian space probes, such as Ranger IV and Luna 9, which delivered photographs from only a few miles above the lunar surface, man's search for knowledge of the moon has been conducted from a distance of a quarter of a million miles.

No longer. Soon man himself will walk on the lunar surface. In a very short time Project Apollo will carry three Americans from the launching pad at Cape Kennedy to an orbit about the moon. Then the Lunar Module will peel off the Apollo and arrow down to the moon. As it comes closer to the surface, man will, for the first time, see with his own eyes the landing site so carefully selected from the dozens of possibilities sent back by robot explorers such as Orbiter and Surveyor.

If the site looks good, the retro rockets will fire, and the little buglike vehicle will descend slowly, settling lower and lower on its column of thrust. Finally, it will be down on the lunar surface, the hatch will be popped, and first one and then another astronaut will descend to the lunar surface. The incredible adventure will have begun.

What is it like, this moon that has partnered our career about the sun perhaps since the world began? It pulls our oceans, causing our tides. It lighted our nights when there were no other sources of light. It was a means of counting our days and our seasons when first we learned to grow things. But always the moon was distant. Now it is near. Soon, men will tread upon its surface. What is it like?

The moon has a diameter of 2160 miles and a total area less than that of North and South America. The gross surface of the moon is quite well

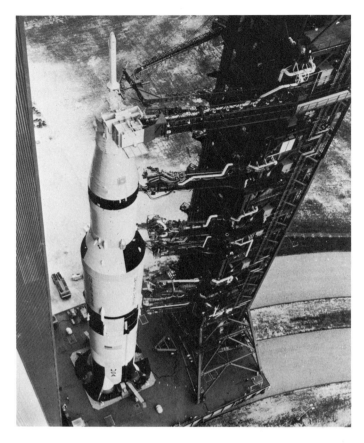

The 363-foot, three-stage Saturn 5 and the Apollo spacecraft being transported from the huge Vehicle Assembly Building at Cape Kennedy to Launch Pad A for an unmanned test flight. *(NASA)*

known. It has mountains, craters, broad flat plains called "seas," long cracks or clefts, and extended raylike lines that streak out from some of the craters.

The craters have tantalized men more than any other feature of the moon. There are too many to count, and they range in size from the gigantic Bailly, with an area of more than 25,000 square miles, down to tiny pockmarks that barely pit the surface. The craters vary not only in size but also in appearance. In some, high terraced walls like the ramparts of an ancient fortress form the crater boundary, and massive peaks poke jagged fingers up from the center of the crater floor. Others have lower, crumbling walls and no trace of central mountains. The floors of some craters flash with the reflected light of the sun, whereas others appear as black as a mine shaft.

But the face of the moon may not be completely foreign. In close-up photos taken by unmanned vehicles, some lunar craters look remarkably similar to earth craters in Iceland. Rocks spilling across the undulant slopes of a lunar "sea" look as if they had been formed by the same kind of geologic events that tumbled acres of rocks in the Canary Islands.

The most remarkable difference is in the lack of air on the moon. There is no weather, only the march of day and night that swings temperatures wildly through the lunar vacuum—from 225 degrees Fahrenheit in the sunlight to 250 degrees below zero in the dark. Although these conditions are extreme, they pose no problems for survival that cannot be solved by evolving technology.

From the first manned landing on the moon we will swiftly and inevitably move on to establish a semipermanent base. The biggest questions about

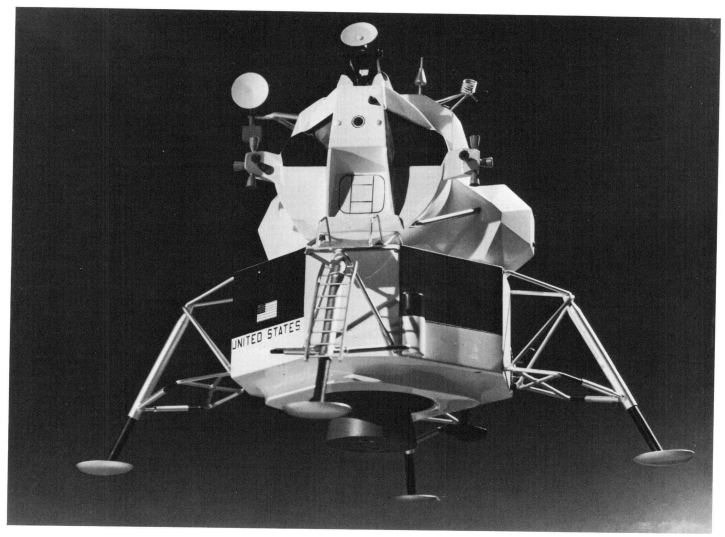

The Lunar Module of the Apollo spacecraft will separate
from the main vehicle while in lunar orbit, to land on
the surface of the moon. Designed for a planet where
there is no air, the LM needs neither wings nor control
surfaces. *(Grumman)*

lunar colonies seem to focus on the time scale. "My estimation is that in the year 2000 our activities on the moon can be best compared with our present activities in Antarctica," declares Wernher von Braun, the German-born director of NASA's Marshall Space Flight Center. "As far as technical feasibility is concerned, I think it is fair to say that in 1976 we could have a semi-permanent, or even a permanent small station on the moon—a kind of Little America where astronauts and scientists could stay, say for half a year and then be relieved by another ship arriving there rotating the crews."

Another German-born space pioneer, Krafft Ehricke, of the Autonetics Corporation, sees the timetable speeded up considerably. "At the beginning of the 21st century," he says, "we will probably have progressed on the moon to the point where we have largely self-sufficient lunar bases and where we now start utilizing the moon. Lunar hotels, lunar launch sites, a large deep space instrumentation facility for communication at a very high frequency and possibly laser frequencies across the entire solar system and even communication with interstellar probes by 1990 would probably be located on the moon."

Whatever the time span, it is inevitable that man will colonize the moon, and the gravest problems that face him are those of life support. Man is a fragile creature at best. Let his body temperature vary just a few degrees and he dies. Alter only slightly the concentration of gases he breathes and he dies. Increase or decrease the amount of pressure on his body more than a few pounds and he will implode or burst. Every aspect of his anatomy and physiology has been carefully tailored by millions of years of evolution to an environment totally unlike that of the moon. Thus, man must

The LM will lower two astronauts to the surface of the moon, while the third remains in the Apollo spacecraft, orbiting the moon. When the mission has been completed, the LM will lift the two men into orbit for docking with Apollo, which will then carry the three astronauts back to earth. *(Grumman)*

A mosaic panorama of the lunar highlands eighteen miles north of the crater Tycho, composed of hundreds of photos, taken by the Surveyor-7 camera, of the view to the northeast of the spacecraft's landing site. *(NASA)*

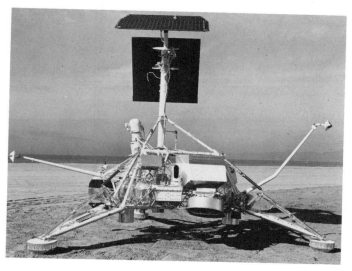

A model of the Surveyor spacecraft, a series of seven robot explorers that soft-landed on the moon and sent back thousands of pictures and other data about the lunar surface. *(NASA)*

Wernher Von Braun, Director of the Marshall Space Flight Center in Huntsville, Alabama, envisions the establishment of lunar colonies, similar to those in Antarctica, that will thrive by the year 2000.

take his environment with him. At first it will be in the form of a shell or envelope in which he can be protected from the extremes his body simply cannot withstand. Such a space suit will be far more complex than those already worn into space by Russian and American astronauts. The prototypes now being built contain bellows-like joints at knees, shoulders, elbows, and thighs to give the wearer some freedom of movement. Over the suit will be baggy coveralls sheathed with a metallic film to reflect the intense solar radiation. The suit will also have a laminated self-sealing liner that, if punctured by micrometeorites, will absorb much of the shock of impact while the lining stops up any holes and maintains enough pressure to permit the lunar explorer to get back to base.

The major task of life support, however, will be carried on by a back pack containing a heat pump and an air conditioner to maintain the wearer at a comfortable seventy-eight degrees inside his suit. Oxygen and power supplies and components to remove carbon dioxide, odor, and water vapor will also be included in what will probably be a thirty-pound pack. On the moon, however, where there is only one sixth of the earth's gravity, the pack would be a mere five pounds.

Such suits and packs will be for trips outside the protective environments of what will, by the year 2001, be a fairly major settlement on the moon. It will be a colony that has conquered its environment to a large extent and may be on the way toward self-sufficiency. To achieve this state, it must close its ecological cycle—that is, find or manufacture within itself the food, water, shelter, power, and atmosphere necessary to sustain human life. Initially, many, if not all, of these necessities will be trucked up by rocket from earth, but even-

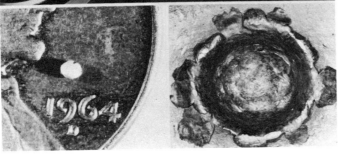

This huge electrothermal gun fires tiny glass pellets simulating micrometeoroids traveling at speeds of twelve miles per second, to test the destructive power of micrometeoroids on the airless surface of the moon. A test bullet is shown on the penny to the right of Lincoln's chin. At lower right is a close-up of the crater blasted by the bullet in a metal target. *(North American Aviation)*

tually the lunar colonists must find within their own environment the means of survival.

The first colonists will probably gain temporary shelter in the depleted fuel stages of the Lunar Modules that carried them onto the moon. But it is to the moon itself that man must look for the materials with which to build any sort of permanent colony. In the absence of an atmosphere, there will be no external pressure to push against the pressure generated inside a structure, so that the problem of insulating against leaks is almost certain to limit the size of the buildings considerably. One possible solution is to burrow beneath the lunar surface and use its rocky interior structure as the walls of a colony. Germano di Leonardo, a research engineer at the General Electric Company, envisions rockets carrying nuclear explosives crashing through the surface of the moon and exploding at a predetermined depth. The blast would gouge out a round chamber beneath the surface. After decontamination of the radioactivity, a tough plastic membrane would be inserted in the cavity, snugly fitting the spherical cave. The membrane would then be pumped full of breathable air. Will such a system work?

Using chunks of pumice rock quarried in Utah, which is believed may resemble the rock that forms the upper layers of the lunar surface, di Leonardo has performed blast experiments that indicate the method is feasible. "It is apparent," he says, "that the explosion breaks down the porous structure of the pumice into fine particles and moves the particle matter radially outward from the detonation center."

Although the original air supply for a colony will be carried up from earth, much as a diver carries his breathing mix in tanks on his back, the colony will swiftly have to make its own air. To do this, in fact to survive at all, the colony will require power, plentiful, dependable power. On earth our power comes from an abundance of swift flowing water and a once bountiful supply of carboniferous fuels—oil, coal, natural gas. The moon offers virtually no hope of providing either form. But power can be packaged, carried, and generated by other sources. Nuclear energy is a vast power source technologically available right now, which has the advantages of portability, economy, and efficiency. Nuclear-electric SNAP generators (Systems for Nuclear Auxiliary Power) are already proliferating throughout the space program and in Atomic Energy Commission projects here on earth. The SNAP-8 furnishes thirty-five to fifty kilowatts of power from a unit not much larger than a portable typewriter—enough power, experts estimate, to run a thirty-five man lunar colony. Larger, more powerful SNAP generators could be built as well as permanent and much larger nuclear power plants of the type now furnishing electric power to many communities on earth.

Still another rich and readily available power source will be the sun itself. Solar-energy batteries are already powering some small satellites and instruments in space. On the moon, where there is no atmosphere to absorb the radiant energy, the sun might provide enough energy to answer virtually all our power needs on the moon.

One scientist, Zdenek Kopal, of the British Interplanetary Society, foresees giant reflectors spotted on the surface of the moon and in strategic orbit about it to capture the sun's radiation. The

A "hard" space suit, designed to protect the astronaut against such hazards as micrometeoroids, is treated in an altitude chamber that simulates the airless state of the moon. The buoyant harness device about the astronaut's waist simulates the low gravitational pull that will be experienced on the moon. *(Lockheed)*

85

energy would then be focused at specific points on the lunar surface, where it would be transformed into electric power.

For such smaller power requirements as would be needed to run appliances and tools on the moon, still another source may be found in a so-called biological battery. Algae, the aquatic plants that include pond scum and practically all seaweeds and which may be the most ubiquitous forms of plant life on earth, will certainly be cultivated on the moon—for food, as a major component in the carbon-dioxide–oxygen conversion cycle, and as a source of supplementary power. In the laboratory, alga colonies have been linked to flasks containing the bacteria of human waste. The link is a chemical "bridge" that allows electrically charged particles present in the two cultures to flow back and forth. The result is a usable current flow large enough to run small appliances. The algae-bacteria combination is actually a biological fuel cell.

Algae may be the single most important life form, and this includes man, to be brought to the moon. For they will unquestionably be the most important component in the lunar food chain. Algae feed on wastes such as feces and, in absorbing wastes, grow at an extremely rapid rate. The intense sunlight available on the moon would provide the key for the photosynthesis process by which algae transform wastes into virtually pure protein.

At a farm in Lancaster, California, NASA grows algae in water tanks into which human fecal wastes are sluiced. The algae absorb the wastes and thus purify the water. Then the algae are separated from the water, dried, and cut into blocks that could be fed to humans. Unfortunately, algae are not one of man's most digestible foods, nor his most aesthetic.

Among the experiments to be carried out during the first few days of manned exploration are subsurface drilling operations. Designed to penetrate the moon's crust to depths of more than one hundred feet, these experiments can provide important clues to the formation and internal composition of the moon.

A possible shelter for post-Apollo moon excursions is this expandable stay-time extension module, or STEM. Almost thirteen feet in length and seven feet in diameter, the STEM is designed to house and support astronauts on the lunar surface for periods up to two weeks. *(Goodyear Aerospace Corporation)*

Thus, a better method is to extend the food chain by feeding the algae to domestic animals, such as chickens, and then to eat the chickens.

Despite the efficiency of algae as a water purifier, they will not be able to support wholly a colony's water needs. Water is the key to man's life on the moon. Some experts feel that water may be found on the moon, perhaps in the form of ice in dark crevasses or caves never touched by the sun. What is more likely is the possibility of liberating water from the stones of the moon. All evidence indicates that an abundance of volcanic rock litters the crust of the moon. In Bend, Oregon, rock formations similar to those thought to be found on the moon have been used by Douglas Aircraft geologist Dr. Jack Green to "squeeze" water from stone. The rocks are crushed and then baked in an airtight container at a temperature of 300 degrees centigrade. Water boils out of the rocks and is distilled and collected at a rate of one gallon per cubic foot of rock. A lunar colony's water needs might be met by a small rock cooker processing ten cubic feet of rock per hour.

If water can be found or manufactured on the moon, it may ultimately free a colony from another of its major import needs—food. The average man needs only one and a half to two pounds of food a day, but he needs six to ten pounds of water. It may be possible to close the water cycle by reprocessing wastes and to close the food cycle later.

A variety of methods will be used to accomplish this. No one expects the moon to furnish soil anything like that found on earth. Thus, there are no plans to grow food on the moon in the way we normally do on earth. Rather, hydroponics—the science of growing plants in water, without soil—

In this artist's concept, astronauts unload a mobile laboratory called a Molab from a lunar module prior to surface exploration of the moon, planned for the early 1970s.

Called a lunar landing research vehicle, this flying unit has a turbofan engine at its center to enable an astronaut to explore a ten-mile range of the moon's surface. Light enough to be carried in the rocket that launched the astronauts, the unit could be fueled from reserve tanks of the LM that landed the astronauts on the moon. *(NASA)*

One form of lunar transportation might be this rocket-powered "pogo stick," designed to give the astronauts a hopping range of twenty-four miles over the lunar terrain.

will be employed by the lunar farmers. The water is enriched with the nutrients needed by plants. Seeds are then planted in a covered water trough, raised to maturity, and harvested.

The reduced gravity of the moon will yield larger fruits and vegetables, and the intense, unfiltered sunlight will enable lunar colonists to grow several crops in a shorter period of time than would be possible on earth. The development of farming on the moon will serve another function besides filling the colonists' bellies. Says Dr. Sanford Siegal, a research biologist at the Union Carbide Research Laboratory, "People living under the most austere conditions will still try to grow a geranium on the window sill, and I think in space, all the more, the tie to the earth that some sort of green thing growing represents—could be a very significant psychological factor. The food it would provide, if we used an ordinary garden type of plant or cultivated plant, is, of course, immediately familiar to our digestive systems and has perhaps an advantage of a direct food source over the algae which has attracted a great deal of attention in recent years. In any case, some kind of processing and some kind of a multistep food cycle would have to be set up under these conditions."

Under any conditions man's major food need is for protein—animal protein—and this might initially be provided on the moon by chickens and rabbits. Research done by the U.S. Department of Agriculture indicates that these two species have the highest ratios for converting food intake into protein-rich products. They grow and reproduce at extremely rapid rates, making replacement of eaten animals relatively easy. A farm of 600 chickens would provide ten colonists with three chickens a week each, plus an egg for breakfast every morning.

To vary the menu, a small batch of rabbits might be added to the lunar farm. Rabbits grow to maturity in six months and their prolific breeding habits —four litters of ten each year—are well known. As a result of short gestation periods and rapid maturation, rabbits and chickens might be readily bred into hardy strains that would quickly adapt to the difficult environment of the moon.

Eventually the lunar farm may come more and more to resemble its terrestrial counterpart if the settlers want it so. Cattle, pigs, and sheep could be shipped from the earth to the moon in an embryonic form. At Washington State University, Dr. E. B. E. Hafez is developing transplant techniques that will permit the transfer of an entire herd of cattle, in embryonic form, into the womb of a rabbit. The rabbit, serving as a prenatal foster mother, would then be shipped to the moon, where the embryos would be transplanted to larger animals or to artificial wombs until birth.

Although cattle and other farm animals such as pigs and sheep return only ten calories for every 100 they consume, when space and power are available to sustain them, they will be established on the moon as a sort of psychological reminder of home.

The moon will pose some problems to animal husbandry, however, since muscle tone is lost quickly in reduced gravity. To prevent the atrophy of muscle tissue, the ancient Japanese technique of cattle rubdowns (perhaps updated with the use of vibrators) to increase the flavor will be employed to maintain the maximum percentage of muscle protein to fat. The human colonists will have reg-

An artist's concept of a semipermanent base providing shelter for six men after they land on the lunar surface. Connected to the shelter is a fuel-regeneration unit that also houses an astronomy laboratory.

Eventually, the LM may become a sort of lunar taxi, ferrying passengers and equipment from orbiting spacecraft to the surface of the moon.

ular exercise to keep their own bodies from running to fat.

Fish could also be added to the lunar diet. The now well-developed techniques of raising fish in hatcheries from egg to maturation can be readily adapted to the moon. The most sophisticated approach would be to have the fish feed on the residues of the hydroponics and algae farms and thus add another link to the ecological chain that will provide man with the essentials of food and water in an alien and barren world.

The moon could, if desired, be provided with an atmosphere of its own. Franz Zwicky, professor of astrophysics at California Institute of Technology,

The space between earth and moon, called cis-lunar space, may be filled with Apollo spacecraft, modified for orbital missions. The upper left picture shows a possible six-man laboratory that contains a command module for living quarters and a bubble-shaped appendage for biomedical experiments. The upper right version of such a laboratory has winglike solar panels to tap the sun's energy for power. *(North American Aviation)* has proposed a plan to do just that. The first step would be to increase the mass of the moon either by sending large masses of waste materials up from the earth or by shrinking the diameter of the moon in half while keeping its mass constant through nuclear explosions that would fuse large parts of the moon. A heavy gas such as carbon dioxide would then be held by the increased gravity of the smaller surface area. A portion of the carbon-dioxide atmosphere thus established could then be vented, along with shafts of sunlight, to the under-

A two-man orbiting laboratory in which the command module itself is crammed with experiments and equipment rather than additional men. *(North American Aviation)*

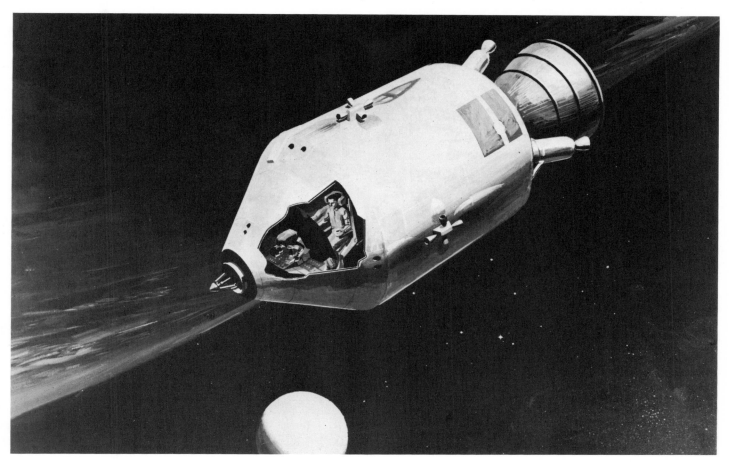

ground plant farms, where it would be converted into oxygen for the lunar colonists.

Giving the moon an atmosphere, however, might rob it of its most valuable resource. In its present airless state, the moon is a giant laboratory. Its unlimited vacuum, reduced gravitational field, and attenuated magnetic field would allow us to design and carry out experiments in solid-state and plasma physics that can scarcely be conceived of on earth. Because it is, in effect, an enormous vacuum chamber, space vehicles and pure chemicals and metals might be tested and produced on the moon under conditions unequalled on earth.

It is as an astronomical observatory that the moon will be of inestimable value. The most immediate benefit is the lack of an atmosphere. On earth the atmosphere serves only to distort and blur the light coming from the other stars and planets of the universe. Weather, the result of an atmosphere, also plays a major role in reducing the time an astronomer can spend observing the heavens through a telescope.

On the moon, the increase in visibility that results from the lack of an atmosphere would mean that only two telescopes—one at each pole—would be needed to view the entire celestial sphere of the universe. Telescopes on the moon could be much larger than those built on earth, because the pull of gravity, which sags the reflector and thus limits the size of the telescope, would be considerably reduced.

Astronomers estimate that the greater visibility and lack of weather will increase the power of the telescopes by a factor of ten. The largest optical telescope ever built, the two-hundred-inch reflector at Mount Palomar in California, for example, can

This semipermanent lunar base is a twelve-man complex. The individual units are covered with lunar surface material to protect them from heat and cosmic radiation.

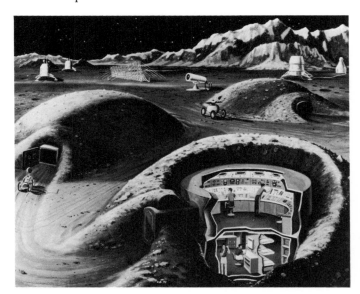

Early in the 21st century there may be several full-scale lunar cities such as this one envisioned by an artist. A combined surface and underground complex, the city obtains its power from a nuclear-power station, shown in the extreme top left of the drawing. Moving sidewalks provide transportation throughout the city and connect it with the moon port.

peer three billion light years into space. The same telescope on the moon might then reach out to the very limits of the universe itself. Not only optical telescopes, but radio astronomy—the branch of astronomy that "views" radio signals from space—will also benefit from a station on the moon. On the far side of the moon radio astronomers would be insulated from the earth's radio emissions and receive, without atmospheric distortion, the radio signals from a billion suns. Such would be the clarity of reception that astronomers could pick and choose the emissions they wished to study with an ease and speed that would vastly increase their working efficiency.

The most salient fact about the moon, its lack of an atmosphere, which led earlier astronomers to classify it as a dead, barren world, is probably its greatest asset. Everything from manufacturing to the exploration of the solar system is based upon this fact. On earth, whole industries—electronics, communications, pharmaceuticals—are dependent in one way or another upon the creation of at least a partial vacuum. A good vacuum on earth is expensive; a good, large vacuum is impossible. "On the moon," says science writer Arthur C. Clarke, "there will be a hard vacuum of unlimited extent outside of every airlock."

What this will mean to the economic viability of a lunar colony can only be guessed at. The transistor industry will surely be one of the first to be established. An electroplating industry that depends upon a vacuum is another, and the melting and fusing of special alloys yet another. Even the most prohibitive of freight charges—the cost of shipments between earth and moon—might not deter the shipping of such transistor materials as silicon monocrystal, which must be produced in a vacuum and which, in 1967, cost $595 a pound on earth.

Still another export commodity might be power. Nikolai N. Semenov, a Russian physicist, at one time suggested converting the moon into a gigantic power plant. Semenov reasoned that every unit of the lunar surface receives three times as much solar radiation as one unit of the earth's surface, since there is no atmosphere to absorb part of the sun's rays. "Thus," he states, "if man succeeded in covering the entire surface of the moon with semiconductors and photoelements of great efficiency and found a means of conveying the electric power produced—by radio waves, for instance—the moon could become a gigantic power station for the whole earth with a power of dozens of trillions of kilowatts."

The moon may provide power of another sort—power to launch the space probes that now seem, even with nuclear propulsion, to be beyond the resources of the earth. The moon could be used as a sort of space gun that would use its own rotation and lack of atmosphere to fire rockets into deep space. Vehicles could leave the moon without burning any of the fuel they carried; for all the work of take-off would be done by fixed power plants on the ground, which could be as large and massive as required. Arthur C. Clarke explains, "To escape from the Earth, a body must reach the now familiar speed of 25,000 miles an hour. At the fierce acceleration of ten gravities, which astronauts have already withstood for very short periods of time, it would take two minutes to attain this speed—and the launching track would have to be doubled. And, of course, any object traveling at such a speed in the lower atmosphere would be instantly burned up by friction. We can forget all about space guns on Earth.

"The situation is completely different on the moon. Because of the almost perfect vacuum, the lunar escape speed of a mere 5200 miles per hour can be achieved at ground level without any danger from air resistance. And, at an acceleration of ten gravities, the launching track need be only nineteen miles long—not four hundred, as on earth. . . ."

With such a capability, the moon will inevitably become a 21st-century jumping-off point for the exploration of the solar system. Moreover, the moon might be able to provide the resources for the manufacture of spaceships directly on the moon, and with the advent of nuclear propulsion and electric rockets that can go enormous distances on small fuel cores, the assault on the stars may well begin from the moon.

Even the crews who man these ships would be better suited to the rigors of space flight if they—like their vehicles—are native to the moon.

"There will be people born on the moon, live there and die there and perhaps never visit the earth," says science writer Isaac Asimov. "I think that they will represent our hope for the future, as far as space exploration is concerned. It will be a lot easier for them to carry out the exploration of the rest of the solar system, than for ourselves to do so, for a variety of reasons.

"I speculated that we might develop two subspecies of men—G and null-G: G representing gravity; null-G representing low or zero gravity. I think there will be sufficient differences, but psychologically and physically, so that neither group will feel completely at home with the other; they'll always be aware of differences. Nevertheless, it also seems to me that it will be the null-G men, the low gravity men, who will be naturals for the exploration of the solar system."

Just how far men of either subspecies will penetrate into the universe remains to be seen. But man is going to the moon, and it is from the moon that he will reach far out into space. His telescopes will comb the heavens to the very frontiers of the universe. From the moon he will truly step out into space, launching first instruments and then men to land on the other planets of our solar system.

5

Mars and Beyond

The speculations and plans for man's space ventures in the 21st century are not the penny-ante dreams of a man with his head hung down and his toes scuffing up the dust. Consider, for example, the capture and mining of an asteroid; the conversion of Venus into a gigantic planetary plantation; the establishment of large, permanent colonies on Mars; the exploration of all the planets of the solar system—these are but a few of the plans being offered right now, as prospective projects for a 21st-century space effort. Some do not require very much imagination to be foreseen as practical; others push credibility to the borders of astonishment. But none push beyond the frontiers of the possible. All that is required for any of these schemes is a means of getting there and back. That means is already on the drawing board in the form of a space vehicle designed to carry men to Mars and back.

Its designer is Dr. Ernst Stuhlinger, Director of NASA's Research Projects Laboratory at the Marshall Space Flight Center in Huntsville, Alabama. Stuhlinger envisions a gigantic ship in the shape of a crossbow—the bow measuring 540 feet across.

At each end of the bow is a giant canister or capsule, each about as large as a sixteen-room house. As it rockets through space, the vehicle will rotate slowly on its axis, providing each capsule with an artificial gravity equal to about a fifth of a G, about as much as a man would feel while walking on the surface of the moon. Communication between the men in the two capsules would be by telephone, but Dr. Stuhlinger also envisions social calls being made by the two crews. "They have an escape hatch in each of the two capsules," he points out, "and they can go out in their space suits and they can just crawl along here. Maybe

Ernst Stuhlinger, director of the Research Projects Division of NASA's Marshal Space Flight Center. *(CBS)*

they have a rope to pull themselves along—there's not much force involved—and they can quite easily go from one end to the other."

Going from the vehicle to the surface of Mars will be only a little more difficult. In the middle of the giant bow is another space vehicle—a landing ship designed to carry the astronauts down to the surface of Mars. The main ship is not designed for a soft landing in the thin atmosphere, and so it will merely orbit Mars while the landing party descends to the surface and makes a preliminary survey. The present plan calls for four weeks of exploration, and then the landing vehicle will carry the astronauts back up to the main ship for the long voyage home.

The key to such an ambitious space journey is the power plant. The trip itself will take 450 days—almost a year and a half—a period of time far in excess of the fuel-carrying capacity of any known chemical rocket. The answer lies in the development of a nuclear engine, a problem that many space scientists think requires nothing more than a large dose of engineering.

There is little question now about our technical ability to develop a vehicle that can reach Mars and return. There is a question of the ultimate gain to civilization. Dr. Stuhlinger answers such questions as follows: "This vehicle will be for the astronauts about what the *Santa Maria* was for Columbus when he came to this country for the first time about five hundred years ago. If he had known at that time that he had discovered a new continent he probably would have said there will be, without doubt, many benefits from the new continent for us and for mankind of which we have no idea as yet."

Columbus searched for a new route to India.

Our space efforts are aimed at exploring an entire planet and then a solar system that contains nine planets. What are they like, these nine planets that circle the sun in stately procession and unvarying routine? Mercury, the smallest and closest to the sun, is probably like the moon—an airless world with a bleak, rocky surface. The starkness of Mercury and its closeness to the sun make it an extremely unlikely candidate for manned exploration.

Venus is next in line, with its face forever hidden by thick clouds that reflect sunlight so well that it is the third-brightest object in the sky. The clouds make Venus one of the most frustrating of bodies, for it passes closer to us than any other planet and

Photographs of a pepper plant that spent forty-five hours in orbit on board Biosatellite II. Scientists believe that under conditions of weightlessness the growth hormone moves to the top of the leaves where the cells continue to grow, thus causing the leaves to curl downward. *(NASA)*

yet we are unable to penetrate the dense clouds that cover its entire surface. But an increasingly sophisticated space technology will enable us to answer many of the questions that now plague us about Venus. The first flyby of Mariner II recorded a surface temperature of 800 degrees Fahrenheit, a finding that was verified by the more recent Mariner V, although the Russian Venus probe in 1967 recorded a temperature of 536 degrees Fahrenheit. Many questions about the planet remain to be answered by more probes, and possibly by robots.

By far, the most fascinating planet for us is Mars. Known as the red planet, it is smaller than Venus or the earth and, at times, approaches to within a mere thirty-five million miles of the earth. It has displayed to some astronomers a still unexplained network of lines called "canals." Mars has a thin atmosphere and, most fascinating of all, there is the possibility that some form of life might exist on it.

Beyond Mars, the character of the solar system changes radically. Instead of finding worlds similar in size and density to our own, we find four huge planets, the smallest of which, Neptune, is about four times as large as the earth.

The largest of the planets is Jupiter, which contains more material than in all the other planets combined. It is one of the so-called gas giants, with a deep, toxic atmosphere made up of ammonia, methane, hydrogen, and other gases. At its top, the atmosphere of Jupiter may be gaseous, but several thousands of miles deep it is thought to be either liquid or frozen in great heavy layers over a solid core of metals that may itself be 40,000 miles across. Jupiter is, in a word, enormous—unquestionably the king of planets.

Artist's concept of a space vehicle in which two capsules whirl at the ends of a 160-foot arm to create artificial gravity in order to avoid the negative effects of prolonged weightlessness. *(North American Aviation)*

Artist's concept of an advanced space vehicle powered by nuclear-explosive systems called pulse units. Ejected successively from a storage chamber and detonated some distance behind the vehicle, the pulse units would liberate high energy that would push the ship through space. *(North American Rockwell Corporation)*

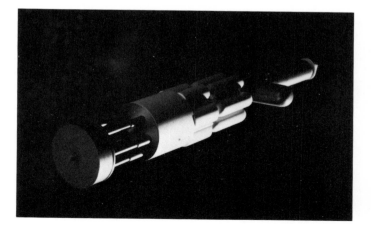

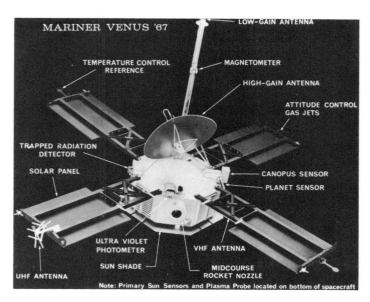

Drawing of the Mariner V spacecraft that flew by Venus at a range of two thousand miles in October 1967. (NASA)

The planet Saturn and its rings, viewed through a sixty-inch telescope. (© 1965, California Institute of Technology and Carnegie Institution of Washington)

The second of the gas giants is Saturn, which is almost twice as far from the sun as Jupiter. Saturn is the spectacular sight of the solar system, with a system of rings made of billions of tiny particles of frozen gas or ice-covered bits of stone that glitter like diamonds about a dowager's neck. Saturn may be entirely gas, without a solid core at all, for its average density is only seventy per cent that of water—about half as dense as Jupiter.

Uranus, the farthest planet that is visible from the earth with the naked eye, is another gas giant. Its chief claim to fame is an elongated orbit that requires eighty-four years to complete a journey about the sun. This lengthy orbit was predicted by early astronomers on the basis of Newton's laws. But as telescopic observation of Uranus plainly showed, its orbit was not quite what it was predicted to be. Either something had to be pulling it off course or Newton's laws of gravitation needed some drastic revision. In 1846 the laws were confirmed rather than revised when a pair of mathematicians calculated the exact position of a planet that would account for the deviation in Uranus's course. In September 23 of the same year astronomers in the Berlin Observatory used the calculations to find Neptune, the hitherto unknown planet that was affecting Uranus's orbit.

Neptune is the densest of the gas giants. It is twice as dense as Jupiter and of almost the same density as the moon. Close observation of Neptune offers some surprising information, for its two moons circle the planet in opposite directions.

The discovery of Neptune seemingly completed a logical, consistent solar system. Four earthlike planets and four gas giants were a neat balance around which certain laws could be constructed. And, even if no one could in his wildest theoretical fancies explain just why there should be such glaring disparities between the gas giants and the four terrene planets, at least the differences were consistent. Then, observations of Neptune showed that still another planet would have to be found to account completely for the aberrations in Uranus's orbit. The American astronomer Percival Lowell predicted its existence, but he died in 1916, without finding it. However, his calculations and insistence led to the discovery, by an astronomer named Clyde Tombaugh, on March 14, 1930, of Pluto, the ninth planet, almost four billion miles away from the sun. It is a planet of extraordinary contradictions that has puzzled astronomers since its discovery. Unlike the gas giants, whose territory it roams in an erratic orbit, it is smaller than the earth, with a period of rotation of 6.4 earth days about its axis. To account for the eccentricity of its orbit and its long rotation period, astronomers believe Pluto to be an escaped moon of Neptune.

These then are the continents to be explored by the 21st-century cosmonauts—huge worlds, so mysterious and so far off that one scarcely dares think of the surprises they hold. But of all the mysteries that lie within the solar system, none has the fascination for us as the question: Is there life there? Will we find it on any planet but our own? "When you look at the size of the universe, at the number of stars in our own star system, the Milky Way system, which is about a hundred and fifty billion, and realize that there are billions and billions of other galaxies like this and that many of these stars, perhaps even all of them, have planets," says Walter Sullivan, science editor of *The New York Times*, "you can only suppose that there must be billions upon billions of worlds, a certain percentage of which are like ours in all the important respects for supporting life. When you think of all this, it's rather silly to think this is the only little speck in that huge universe that has life—intelligent life—on it. So I'm persuaded that there is intelligent life all through the universe. It's as much a part of the universe as the law of gravity."

Exobiology is the study of life beyond the earth. It will be carried out by robot vehicles as well as manned explorations. The Mariner series already used in flybys past Venus and Mars has returned valuable data about the life-supporting conditions on both planets. None of the missions provided evidence of the existence of life on either Venus or Mars, but it did indicate that life was not impossible on Mars. In the rather ponderous language of the exobiologists, a report on the Mariner IV flyby of Mars stated: "We cannot conclude that on Mars the temperature range, the low water content, the very low oxygen tension, or even the high ultraviolet flux necessarily create a challenge that defeats the incredible resourcefulness of self-replicating systems."

"The chance of finding life on Mars is clearly not zero," says Professor N. H. Horowitz, chief of the Bioscience Section of Caltech's Jet Propulsion Laboratory, "but neither is it very high. Scarcity of water is probably the most serious limiting factor for any Martian biology. . . . No permanent body of liquid water can exist there. . . . No terrestrial species could survive under average Martian conditions as we know them, except in a dormant state.

"This is all very depressing news for biologists, but if I have learned anything during six years of association with the space program it is that people with manic-depressive tendencies should stay out of it . . . for one's subjective estimate of the like-

One of a series of photographs of the surface of Mars, taken from a slant range of 8400 miles by Mariner IV, which showed no evidence of the straight-line features called "canals," seen by some astronomers with earth-based telescopes. *(NASA)*

103

lihood of finding life on Mars is liable to undergo violent fluctuations from time to time as new data accumulates.

"The problem is that our data is still very skimpy and has been collected from distances of nine or ten thousand miles above the planet's surface. It is as if a Martian astronomer had tried to answer the question of whether or not there was life on earth."

Such an unlikely event might possibly have happened. Mars has two moons, observed for the first time in 1877, but first unaccountably described by Jonathan Swift in *Gulliver's Travels*, 150 years earlier. The two moons of Mars were named Deimos and Phobos after the horses that drew the chariot of the Greek god of war. The orbits of the two satellites are nearly circular, but something quite strange is happening. According to Bevan P. Sharpless, of the U.S. Naval Observatory, the orbit of Phobos is decaying rapidly, too quickly for a solid satellite of its mass. Phobos is headed for destruction in a comparatively short time, as astronomical events are measured.

No one has satisfactorily explained the decay of Phobos's orbit, but a Russian scientist, Dr. I. S. Shklovskii, of the Sternberg Astronomical Institute in Moscow, has offered an extraordinary explanation. Shklovskii suggests that Phobos is hollow, the same as the artificial satellites we and the Russians have been putting into orbit for the last ten years. He compares Phobos to the balloon satellite Echo I, which responds with a decaying orbit to extremely small amounts of drag. Thus, Shklovskii advances the astonishing proposal that both Demos and Phobos may be hollow, artificial satellites orbited millions of years ago by intelligent beings of a highly advanced civilization.

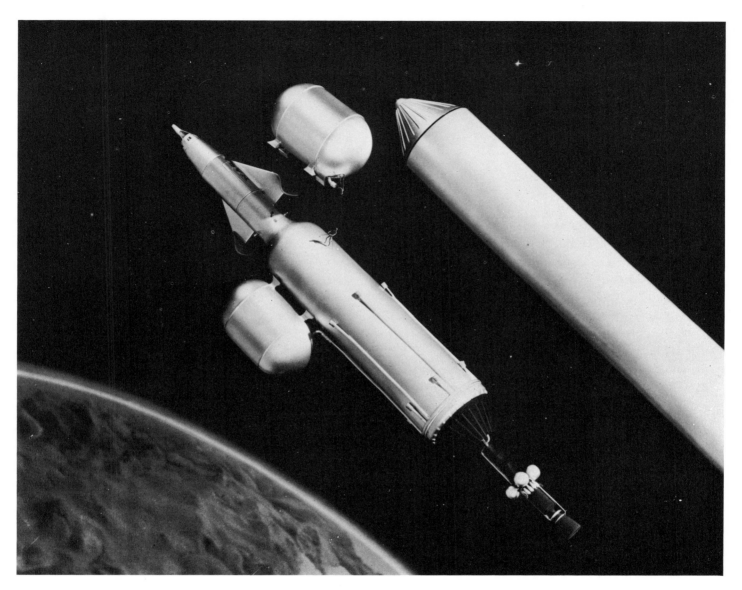

A nuclear-powered rocket designed to land men on Mars
could take on tanks of liquid hydrogen in low earth orbit.
(General Electric)

No one can disprove the Shklovskii theory, nor is it likely that anyone will until we actually land a man on Phobos and have the evidence of first-hand investigation. Until then, the idea of a Martian astronomer at one point in the history of the solar system questioning the existence of life on earth must be accepted as improbable but nonetheless within the bounds of possibility. It is far more probable that if intelligent Martians did exist, their techniques for planetary exploration would have been quite similar to the ones we have developed. Martian probes that merely flew by from a height of several hundred miles above the earth's surface would first detect a corrosive gas called oxygen. In the table of the elements oxygen is one of the most reactive substances, combining readily with almost anything including the volatile compounds of carbon, nitrogen, and hydrogen from which all living organisms on earth are built. Furthermore, the Martian satellites would send back evidence that the earth was almost entirely covered with water, leading biological theorists on Mars to some bizarre conclusions. To an intelligent Martian, the dominant creature on the earth would almost have to be a fish. Biochemist and science writer Isaac Asimov describes the situation this way: "If a Martian were set the task of describing an Earth man—if there were one—he would have to describe one that could live under water. It wouldn't occur to him that the relatively minor portion of the earth which is dry land would see life developed."

By the same token, our robot-eyed views of Mars may be equally misleading. What we need is a much closer look, an on-the-scene appraisal, first by machine and later by men. Voyager is a series of spacecraft designed to soft land on Mars and seek out the life forms that might exist. The devices

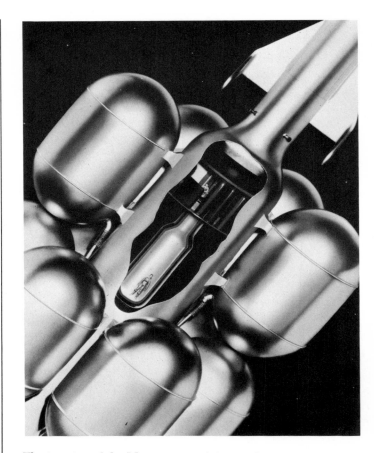

The interior of the Mars spacecraft is seen in cutaway. A two-deck command module would contain the life-support systems, living quarters, a control center, and all the communications and scientific equipment needed for the fifteen-month journey to Mars and back.

106

Two of the four-man crew transfer to the Mars excursion
module and head down toward the surface.
Everything except the absolute minimum of life-support
equipment and a few hundred pounds of soil samples
are left behind on the Martian surface. The final stage of
the landing vehicle uses the first-stage structure as a
launching platform for a return to Mars orbit for docking
with the nuclear-rocket spacecraft.

it will carry are automated biological laboratories
capable of collecting and analyzing samples of the
Martian surface. One design, called the Wolf trap,
after its inventor, Dr. Wolf Vishniac, Chairman of
the Department of Biology at the University of
Rochester, has already been tested under harsh
conditions. Placed on the floor of Death Valley,
it has scooped up samples of the soil and bathed
them in chemicals that revealed the presence of
nucleic acids and proteins, the building blocks of
life. On Mars the results of these and other tests
will be telemetered back to earth.

Such robots may or may not send back evidence
that will support the idea that life exists on Mars.
The possibility that life, even in its most primitive
forms, may not exist there, or even elsewhere in
the solar system, does not discourage the exobiologists. "What we are seeking to clarify," wrote
committee members of the National Academy of
Sciences, in a report entitled *Biology and the Exploration of Mars,* "is the probability of living
organization emerging in the sequence of chemical
change inherent in a planet's history. It is clear that
the positive result of discovering Martian life
would be the greatest clarification, empirically
demonstrating the probability to be high. But it is
not the only result that would be useful. Any knowledge of the history of Martian chemical evolution
will contribute to our total understanding of the
fundamental issues involved."

These fundamental issues are chemical. The
manner in which a series of chemical reactions can
combine a number of compounds into an organization capable of growth and reproduction is purely
and simply a description of life—not merely on
earth but anywhere in the universe. Just how this
process occurs on earth is the subject of intense

study, for it seems reasonable that although the end products may differ widely, the process of life creation should be essentially and chemically similar on any planet located anywhere throughout the universe.

We are beginning to understand this process, which most probably began in the sea, and to reproduce it in the laboratory. Some few billions of years ago, when the earth was very young, the atmosphere was quite unlike the one we breathe today. There was no free oxygen to react with the individual chemical building blocks of life—carbon dioxide, which provided carbon atoms, ammonia, which furnished nitrogen atoms, and water vapor, which supplied a solvent in which the chemical reaction could take place.

What happened in that volatile atmosphere is not quite known, but one theory that has been experimentally reproduced in the laboratory was offered by the great British biologist J. B. S. Haldane. Haldane proposed that ultraviolet light from the sun triggered chemical reactions that linked the carbon and nitrogen into long chains of molecules. "From such reactions, a vast variety of organic substances are made," Haldane noted, "including sugars and apparently some of the materials from which proteins are built up. Today such substances, when left about, decay—that is to say, they are destroyed by microorganisms. But before the origin of life, they must have accumulated till the primitive oceans reached the consistency of hot dilute soup."

Within the soup, the compounds multiplied and changed, producing giant complex molecules, molecules that could in turn produce copies of themselves from the smallest chains of molecules in which they were immersed. It was perhaps at this

In this chamber, called a Mars simulator, a variety of plants are studied under conditions reproducing the Mars environment. With no free oxygen and virtually no water vapor in its atmosphere, it was still possible for young plant shoots to survive. *(Union Carbide Corporation)*

108

time that molecules capable of carrying information—genetic information—were formed, and the entire self-reproducing complex encapsulated in an oily drop rolled up from a film on the surface of the sea. The end result was the creation of the cell, the basic biological unit of organized life.

From that point on these amorphous cells, generalized and with neither purpose nor goal—even survival had not yet been incorporated into the admixture—grew with incredible speed to the outermost limits of the food supply. Then, aeons of random happenings, of accidental chemical combinations, produced the means of converting the sun's energy into food—photosynthesis. From that point to the development of intelligent life is simply a matter of time and luck. The form and viability of such life is another question, dictated by the environment, but of little consequence beyond the overwhelming fact of life itself.

The theories of Haldane, refined and added to by others, have been subjected to the proof of experiment and have stood the test. In the laboratory biologists have succeeded in creating the basic chemical building blocks from which life might be built. Explains Cyril Ponnamperuma, of NASA's Ames Biological Laboratory, "We have a flask, one flask which represents the primitive atmosphere, another flask which represents the primitive ocean. These two are connected. The reaction takes place in the upper regions of the atmosphere and the organic matter synthesizes and collects in the lower flask till one gets something like Haldane's primordial soup.

"In this one finds amino acids, traces of those constituents that can go up and up to make the nucleic acids for example. These are the building blocks from which one gets big polymers, the

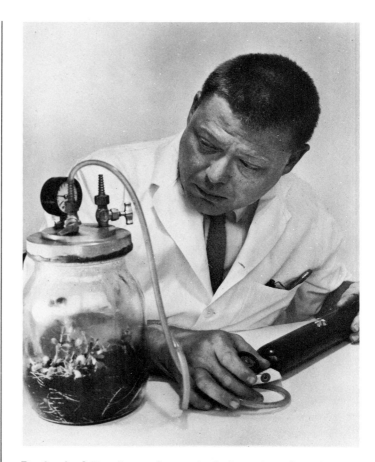

Dr. Sanford Siegal tests the survival of growing plants in a vessel with an ammonia-laden atmosphere resembling that of Jupiter and that of the earth when it was very young. *(Union Carbide Corporation)*

109

Model of an asteroid on which mining operations have begun, as Dr. Krafft Ehricke envisions the scene. Passing above the asteroid is a space vehicle propelled by a thermonuclear-fusion reactor. *(North American Rockwell Corporation)*

Dr. Krafft Ehricke envisions not only asteroid mining but orbiting hotels and hospitals throughout the solar system. *(North American Rockwell Corporation)*

nucleic acids and the proteins which are the basic constituents of living organisms."

With the basic building blocks available, life is almost inevitable. Even on earth the harshest and seemingly barrenest of environments can support some form of life. At the Union Carbide Research Laboratories Dr. Sanford Siegal, a research biologist, confronted a variety of life forms with seemingly impossible environments. In test tubes of lead, copper, and mercury, molds and yeasts survive. Plants grow on copper, which may be a major element of the red-oxide deserts of Mars. Tarantulas are exposed to a constant flux of ultraviolet radiation, as much as bombards Mars in a month. They not only survive but thrive. In another chamber, turtles live under pressures only one tenth that of sea level, approximately the same pressure generated by the thin atmosphere on the surface of Mars. "There's no question," says Dr. Siegal, "about the ease with which common forms of life can adjust to environments which not only don't represent any planet that we know, but also don't represent anything in the history of the evolution of these forms of life on the Earth. What we can see is that all life has a common denominator in its origins; within life itself there exists the capabilities for withstanding all the pieces that we can put together of all the things that we consider to be inhospitable about Mars, so that Earthly life as a whole has built into it every capability needed to live on Mars."

The same technology needed to find life on other planets will also supply the tools and techniques to exploit the raw materials and special environments that exist on them. Dr. Krafft Ehricke, of the Autonetics Corporation, has proposed attempting to clear the atmosphere of Venus and eventually turning the entire planet into arable farm land. "These would be experiments on a global scale and just as the farmer of medieval Europe who had half an acre could hardly understand the Texas rancher with his range of twenty thousand acres, so the little Earth farmer by that time will find it hard to understand that you have a plantation which is the size of a celestial body."

Mining of the planets would be another major possibility for exploitation. Even inhospitable Mercury, a dense planet, may be made to yield from relatively accessible deposits valuable metals such as tungsten, chromium, and nickel, which might be mined by robots. Asteroids might be captured, zipped open with the use of nuclear power to peel out their ore, and then cast back into space. Or the hollowed-out asteroids might serve as satellite colonies to take surplus population from the earth.

The area between the earth and the moon, called cis-lunar space, will also be exploited. Orbiting stations will serve as halfway houses between the earth and its lunar colonies. Others will forecast and control the weather. An oceanographic station in space might scout huge schools of fish. A space vehicle shaped like a giant wagon wheel might serve as an orbiting hospital. Its main advantage would be a range of gravitational pull from weightlessness up to one gravity. At the hub of the vehicle there would be zero gravity, which would increase gradually as you go outward until at the farthest point from the rotational axis one earth gravity is achieved.

Such a hospital already exists in model form at the Autonetics Corporation. One major crop of patients for the hospital would be astronauts returning from lengthy trips during which they were weightless for months or even years. "You don't

A brief period in an orbiting hospital might be an important transition for astronauts returning from long voyages. Each of the wards within the ladder-like extensions can be given an increased gravity as one progresses outward. *(North American Rockwell Corporation)*

Artist's concept of an orbital pleasure dome that spins around its vertical axis, providing artificial gravity for its "rooms." *(North American Rockwell Corporation)*

really want to necessarily dump them right back into one G," explains Dr. Ehricke. "You may put them into one of these wards here and gradually recondition them, at least up to three quarters of a G, before they are released to Earth." Low gravity might provide an exciting medical asset for patients with burns, arthritis, and a host of other infirmities.

The space between the planets and the orbiting vehicles may become an extension of man's ambitions and aspirations. Surely the uses to which space may be put are limited only by the mind of man, and no one has yet set any limits on human imagination. All that is required is the proper catalyst. Says Dr. Ehricke: "We have to have a civilization that needs these things so first we have to explore. Then we start exploiting and as we exploit, the utility effect comes in—we have to have better transportation systems and people get accustomed to the services that result from that exploitation and after they get accustomed to it, they don't want to miss it any more. They need it more and more and the service will be refined more and more and you have included another portion of the universe into the service of man and 'anthropologized' another region of the world—the land, the oceans, the air, space. The civilization of Eric the Red didn't need the discovery of America, but the civilization of Columbus did. Our civilization may not need mining on an asteroid, but the civilization of the 21st century may very well need it. If they do, from the technical standpoint, we are ready."

The lure of space is great, but it has been largely confined to our own neighborhood, our own solar system. For the rest of this century and almost

Each pod in the hotel will have twelve floors of four rooms each. Projected cost is eighty dollars a day per person, presumably with all the comforts of space, including a swiftly changing panorama as the hotel rotates from sunshine to darkness every few minutes. *(North American Rockwell Corporation)*

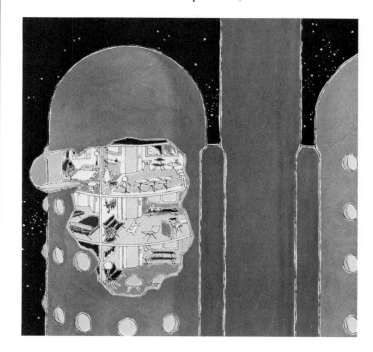

Guests in Krafft Ehricke's orbiting hotel would be able to float about effortlessly inside the "zero-G play pods," where there would be no artificial gravity. *(North American Rockwell Corporation)*

certainly for all of the 21st century this backwater of space will not only be more than enough for us to explore and exploit, it will also be all that will be within our technological reach. With our current capabilities, the round-trip journey to Mars is an eighteen-month proposition. With a generation of work on a nuclear rocket, we might build up our speeds by a factor of ten or even a hundred, until velocities of hundreds of miles a second are achieved. But the nearest star is nearly a million times farther from the earth than is Mars.

Still, it is not beyond our ambition, for the escape velocity needed to overcome the gravitational pull of the sun at a point in the earth's orbit is only about eight miles per second more than the seven miles per second needed to escape the earth's gravity. There remains only the overwhelming distances to be covered. The nearest star, Alpha Centauri, is four and one half light years away and our pitiful spacecraft, even one powered by fusion, could attain only a small fraction of the speed of light. At the speed of say 2,500,000 miles per hour—*one hundred times* that of present-day rocket velocities—it would still take an instrumented probe about 12,000 years to arrive on target.

Will we be able to overcome the technological difficulties inherent in an interstellar journey? Can man, from this insignificant planet in a remote corner of a vast and densely star-populated universe, challenge that great unknown? These will be the questions that can be answered only in the 21st century when the tools and techniques for space exploration and exploitation become equal to our consuming interest in the rest of the universe around us.

During the 21st century, a close-up view of the rings of Saturn might be a commonplace experience not only for astronaut explorers but perhaps even for adventuresome vacationers on a holiday space excursion. *(North American Aviation)*

6

The Deep Frontier

Much of the glamour of the 21st-century explorations will remain affixed to deep space probes and manned landings on the other planets of our solar system. But not all the effort of exploration will be lavished on space. Much closer to home there is a world that holds more secrets than the far side of the moon. It is a world unlike any other, for insofar as astronomers can tell, earth is the only planet in the solar system that has an ocean. There is only one ocean, and it covers 140,000 square miles—seventy-one per cent of the earth's surface. It is a vast heat engine that powers the meteorological cycles that make life possible on earth. It is the ancestral home of all life on earth and has within its vastness the smallest and largest of all creatures. From here man's precursors crawled onto the land three hundred and sixty million years ago.

Since that time it has been, for man, a place of incredible hostility, of cold, dark, and crushing pressures, a world without air and with scant sunlight, a world of enormous challenge that has never been fully accepted.

"You have to face one thing," said M. Scott Carpenter, who by virtue of his thirty days of living underwater in a sea laboratory, became America's only astronaut-aquanaut, "work in the deep water is just not as glorious a pursuit in the minds of most people as a flight to the moon. Men have dreamed of flying to the moon since they first saw the moon. Not so for the bottom of the sea. It's a cold, dirty place and you can't see very far; you can't go down and take pictures that thrill the world, and it just doesn't enjoy the popular support that space flight does."

Athelstan Spilhaus, former Dean of the Institute of Technology, University of Minnesota, declares:

This 30-foot "sandfall," photographed in a submarine canyon off the coast of Baja California, is formed by currents that spill sand from nearby beaches into the canyon. *(Scripps Institution of Oceanography)*

"With minerals resting on it, nutrients sinking into it, geologic history locked in its sedimentary layers, and petroleum beneath it, the sea's bottom is at least as interesting and certainly more useful to mankind than the moon's backside."

We do not approach the ocean completely bereft of knowledge or desire, but there is little doubt that between now and the 21st century, we shall probably learn more about it than we have learned in all the years since man first sailed out from shore with the terrifying fear that he would fall off the edge of the earth.

The first target of this new oceanographic exploration will begin at our very doorsteps. The ocean bottom begins as a shoulder of land called the continental shelf. Ringing each of the continents and extending outward from a few to hundreds of miles, the shelves are covered by water to a depth of six hundred feet.

"That they are submerged at all," says Joseph B. MacInnis, of Ocean Systems, Inc., "is an accident of this epoch's sea level; the ocean basins are filled to overflowing, and the sea has spilled over, making ocean floor of what is really a seaward extension of the coastal topography. Geologically, the shelf belongs more to the continents than to the oceans. Its basement rock is continental granite rather than oceanic basalt and is covered largely with continental sediments rather than abyssal ooze."

Between the surface and the bottom of the continental shelf lies a world of infinite variety, of great fish and small, of waving fields of vegetation and creatures that might have stepped out of some psychedelic wonderland. On this shelf are mineral and protein treasures that stagger the imagination. One expert opinion is that the rocks of the continental shelf surrounding the United States may eventually yield, with modern production and conservation methods, as much as twenty billion barrels of petroleum and one hundred and fifty billion cubic feet of natural gas. Another estimate places the potential wealth of the continental shelves as the equivalent of finding another continent the size of Africa. But even beyond mere mineral wealth lies the wealth of knowledge that awaits us, knowledge of a vast and mysterious world that has beckoned, bedazzled, and savaged man since time began on earth. But before we can hope to study the sea around us, we must explore the depths beyond the shelf, where the sun never penetrates.

At the edge of the continental shelf it is as if some giant trap door had been sprung and the bottom fallen out from under. The shelf becomes a plunging slope scarred by canyons and sand falls. This is the continental slope, the largest and highest natural boundary in the world, plummeting more than two miles to the bottom of the sea, where it forms the steep walls of an enormous basin. The deep ocean basin is a dark, flat plain, stretching for hundreds of miles. It lay unknown to man for untold aeons. Its discovery in 1947 by survey vessels of Columbia University's Lamont Geological Laboratory was a startling example of the truly enormous mysteries the sea is capable of concealing.

Beyond the abyssal plain, two miles beneath the surface of the sea, are mountains and valleys, rises and rolling bottom, and great rocky escarpments. Then, there are the trenches, great gouges that spike downward as much as six or more miles into the sea floor. Just as it seems the ocean has exhausted its bag of geological tricks, out pops another, more startling than the last. Thus it is that midway across the Atlantic Ocean bottom there

The Nansen bottle, a standard tool of the oceanographer, collects sea water at specified depths and then is brought to the surface for analysis. Thermometers on the bottle record the temperature of the water at the depth it was collected. *(Scripps Institution of Oceanography)*

FLIP, the 355-foot floating instrument platform, in a horizontal position at the research site. (*Scripps Institution of Oceanography*)

rears up a great, curving spine of submarine mountains, hundreds of miles across and thousands of feet above the ocean floor. Above the peaks of virtually all of the ridge lies a blanket of water several thousand feet deep. Here and there peaks actually pierce the surface to form islands such as Pico in the Azores, Ascension, Tristan de Cunha, and Bouvet. This is the mid-Atlantic ridge, which runs from the tip of Iceland down around the tip of Africa and up into the Indian Ocean. There it links to a ridge that stretches like an outflung arm eastward, below Australia and into the eastern Pacific, then curves north to arrow through Easter Island and the Galapagos, to butt up finally against the western shelves of North America. The ridge system is forty thousand miles long and equal in area to Europe, Asia, and Africa combined. Save for the continents themselves it is the largest geographical feature of the earth.

To explore the sea and its mysterious environs, oceanographers are developing some strange devices. Until very recently, research into the ocean was largely limited to the classic Nansen bottle,

Like a fence post driving itself into the ground, FLIP puts three hundred feet of her length beneath the seas. (*Scripps Institution of Oceanography*)

Fully erect in the water, FLIP becomes a stable four-story building with laboratories and living quarters for twelve people. *(Scripps Institution of Oceanography)*

which hung over a ship's side and brought up samples of water from varying depths, and the more sophisticated technologies of World War II, such as sonar, the underwater counterpart of radar. But now, the ships themselves are being designed as research vehicles. One of the most bizarre and useful of these is called FLIP, for Floating Instrument Platform. FLIP is designed to provide the most stable platform ever put to sea, which it does by taking advantage of the fact that most wave motion occurs on and just below the surface. While underway FLIP looks not unlike other ships, but once on its scientific station it behaves in a most unship-like manner. The 355-foot FLIP floods its after tanks (ballast tanks make up eighty-five per cent of its length) and thus drives itself like a fence post below the surface turbulence. It takes about fifteen minutes for the transition from ordinary-looking ship into something resembling the Loch Ness monster. When FLIP is in a vertical position, its bow—containing four stories of laboratories and living quarters for twelve people—rears fifty-five feet above the surface. Within these floating four stories all of the equipment—everything from fathometers to galley stewpots—swivels on brackets, so that afloat or upended, the work goes on. To perform its myriad research tasks, FLIP has remained in an upright position for as many as ten days.

Man himself must descend into the depths to explore at first hand that which is hidden from his view on the surface. He will do it in the submarine, just as Alexander the Great did it in a crude diving bell about 330 B.C. Alexander descended some fifty feet beneath the surface of the Aegean Sea. When he was hauled back up, he supposedly offered this description of the deeps: "Everything down there

Deep Diver, a research submersible designed by Edwin A. Link. *(Union Carbide Ocean Systems)*

Edwin A. Link, inventor of aviation's Link Trainer and now an oceanographer, is shown talking to Jon Lindbergh, at right, son of the famed Lone Eagle and noted as a diver and marine biologist.

eats everything else." Only recently have we developed the technology to go much deeper than Alexander's dive or add to his scientific observations.

The shape of 21st-century submarines and much of the impetus for undersea research may be seen in the sudden proliferation of deep-diving research vehicles sliding down the ways to answer industrial and government research needs. Perhaps a sort of watery NASA might be created to speed up the exploration process, for the needs of both the space and ocean environments are strikingly similar. Both areas call for manned and unmanned vehicles, for men to live and work for long periods of time in a hostile environment, and for the development of closed-cycle systems that will sustain life in these environments.

The earliest of the deep-diving research vehicles were bathyspheres, round balls of steel, scarcely changed in design from the barrel in which Alexander made his famous descent. The bathyscaphe is a movable modification of the bathysphere. The U.S. Navy's *Trieste* is typical of this class, and similar vehicles will be used even into the 21st century, for no other design has proved capable of surviving the great depths of the abyssal plains and the even deeper trenches that spike them. The bathyscaphes are plodding, ungainly, and limited in their time on bottom. Their one asset is the ability to withstand the enormous, crushing pressures of the depths—nine thousand pounds per square inch at twenty thousand feet. Ninety-eight per cent of the ocean is less than twenty thousand feet deep, and so maneuverability can replace the structural ability to withstand great pressures.

The *Aluminaut* is a compromise vehicle. It carries a crew of three and can descend to a depth of 16,000 feet. Equipped with wheels, the *Alumi-naut* can actually drive over the sea floor and provide the scientist-observer with an unparalleled view of bottom topography. In its bow is an array of sophisticated mechanical hands called manipulators, which can be used to drill into the sea floor for core samples and to scoop up rocks or even passing marine life.

Most of the undersea technology, however, is aimed at highly maneuverable vehicles that can operate freely in the vertical area from just below the surface to six thousand feet. By the 21st century fleets of submersibles capable of going to twenty thousand feet regularly and easily will be a reality. But by the 21st century research will not be the only or even the most important function of the submersible. Work in the depths will be a major industry, and specially designed submarines will be built for this purpose. The prototype of such a workboat is *Deep Diver*, a revolutionary combination of submarine and diving bell. It is capable of carrying man to the depths of the continental shelves, turning him free in the sea, and then carrying him back. It can move from sea bottom to surface with an efficiency never before achieved.

Deep Diver was designed by Edwin A. Link, a retired industrialist turned oceanographer, who many years ago designed the famous aviation Link Trainer. The boat was built by John Perry, a California submarine builder. It weighs eight and a quarter tons, and its crew and equipment can add still another ton. On the surface *Deep Diver* rolls about clumsily, displaying all the grace of a fat lady in a foot race. Its speed is limited. Twenty batteries enable it to cruise on the surface at just two and one half knots for six hours. Submerged, it cruises at only two knots but is far more maneuverable, for underwater is its natural realm—a world much like space, where the directions of up, down, forward, and back are paralleled by movements of pitch, roll, and yaw. *Deep Diver* is in fact something like a spaceship with bow and stern thrusters that rotate in a circle and a main engine that can be turned at right angles. Thus *Deep Diver* can turn inside its own twenty-two-foot length and even go sideways.

Deep Diver carries a crew of four—pilot, observer, and two divers. It was for the divers that the submarine was built. The pilot and observer sit in one compartment of the boat while the two divers use a port or chamber in the second compartment. It is a lock-out chamber that can be pressurized to the point where the ambient air pressure is equal to the pressure of the water outside. This enables the divers to go in and out at will. This is the significance of *Deep Diver* for the 21st century—it provides scientists and engineers with the capability of interacting with the environment rather than simply eyeballing it. At present *Deep Diver* can carry its divers down to 1250 feet—just about twice the depth of the deepest part of the continental shelves. Once on site the divers can explore or work on the bottom for two hours before they must return to the submarine. Umbilical hoses carry power and a breathing gas to the divers from the submarine. In this way *Deep Diver* is the forerunner of a 21st-century technology that will allow man to move between the surface and the sea floor more easily than he now commutes between home and office.

The *Deep Diver* is but one of a host of new submersibles designed to work and research the sea floor. For the moment, each of these vehicles is an expensive proposition. Present-day limitations of

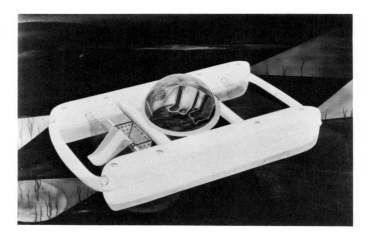

Artist's concept of a durable and inexpensive submersible with a glass hemisphere mounted on a maneuvering sled. The pontoons are made of fiberglass and house the propulsion and power systems of the vehicle. *(Corning Glass Works)*

The Navy's deep submergence rescue vehicle (DSRV) is designed as a means of aiding stricken submarines. It can be carried "piggyback" by a "mother" nuclear submarine to the site of any undersea disaster. When not engaged in rescue work, the DSRV is expected to serve as a research submersible. *(Lockheed)*

launch and support from surface ships bring operating costs to about $4000 a dive. In the search for a more efficient submersible system the Naval Ordnance Test Station at China Lake, California, came up with the idea of a glass submarine. A fifty-six-inch sphere made of glass two and three quarters inches thick is cut in half like an orange and mounted on a Plexiglas boat with motors for maneuverability. The result is a submersible of extreme durability, great structural strength, and low cost. In this design equipment is mounted outside the sphere and is activated by photocell switches and directed light beams on the inside. Initial cost of the submarine is $100,000, with the hope that production costs will drop to $25,000 within five years—a price that both small private industry and oceanographic institutes with modest endowments can afford. By the year 2001 the price may be down to as little as $8000. Perhaps by then two cars, one airplane, and one submarine will be the formula for filling the family garage. Operating costs are relatively low, since no support vessel is necessary. But the chief advantage is the structural strength of glass, which has more buoyancy and greater strength than any other hull material ever used. Glass is uniquely suited to the depths, for it grows stronger as the water pressure increases. The hemispheres, built by Corning Glass Works, are rated to resist pressures of more than 30,000 pounds per square inch, which is equal to depths of 66,000 feet. At that rate, even the deepest part of the ocean, the 36,000-foot Marianas Trench off Guam, will provide only half the pressure the glass submarine can withstand.

Going deep and maneuvering on the bottom are not the only capabilities needed to work and study the depths. Increased bottom time is also urgently

A full-scale mock-up of the inner hull of the DSRV. The three interconnecting spheres that fit inside the outer hull can withstand pressures to a depth of 3500 feet. The skirt at bottom attaches to the distressed sub and is the hatch through which the crew will transfer to safety in the DSRV.

Deep Quest is a research submersible designed to carry scientists and divers to the depths. *(Lockheed)*

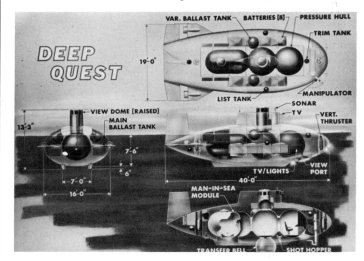

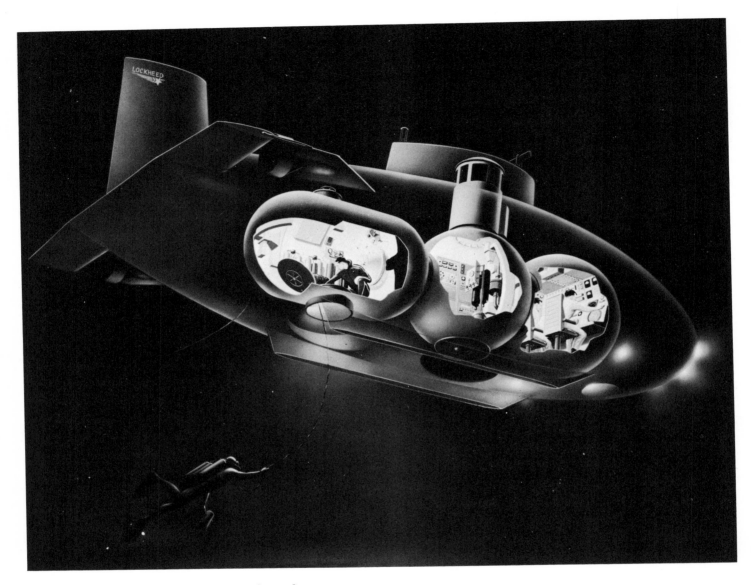

This artist's cutaway view of *Deep Quest* shows the man-in-sea module in operation. The module is a diving chamber with a saturated oxy-helium atmosphere, to be used to move divers from surface to underwater work sites up to a working depth of one thousand feet.

needed, and this requirement will be met by providing the new research submersibles with a nuclear capability. The Navy and the Atomic Energy Commission are now developing jointly a nuclear-powered vehicle designed for deep-submergence research and ocean engineering. The NR-1, as it is called, "will be able to move at maximum speed for periods of time limited only by the amount of food and supplies it carries and will carry a crew of five and two scientists. The vehicle will be able to perform detailed studies and mapping of the ocean bottom, temperature, currents and other oceanographic parameters for military, commercial and scientific uses," according to an official Navy description.

The ultimate in 21st-century oceanographic hardware may then be a remote-controlled underwater vehicle powered by nuclear energy and bristling with instrumentation and servo arms that can do virtually anything man can do. The other half of the package is already in use in the form of a robot submarine called CURV, for Cable-Controlled Underwater Research Vehicle. Effective in depths up to 20,000 feet, CURV is operated by remote control from a console on the surface. Targets are acquired by sonar, then a television camera locks on and sends a picture to the operator on the surface. He guides CURV over the target and activates a set of mechanical claws that make the pick up. CURV has recovered valuable instrument packages from the bottom of the sea, and in its most spectacular feat plucked an H-bomb from the Mediterranean off the coast of Spain.

The new tools and vehicles are revealing much of the unknown, but they are also constraining. Most experts feel that the exploration and work to be done in the ocean will require the presence of man

Deep Quest will be shuttled between diving sites by this "mother" ship dubbed *Trans Quest*. The elevator on which *Deep Quest* rests will lower the sub beneath the surface and pick her up submerged at sea.

125

as a free swimmer. "The first of these reasons," says Dr. John P. Craven, chief scientist of the Navy's Deep Submergence Systems Project, "is that the information processing rate of the human eye is greater by at least an order of magnitude than the most sophisticated electronic equipment we have. The human eye does see a lot more than you can see with television. The second aspect is the capability of the human brain—not so much as a processor, but in terms of a memory unit—is so far superior to any of the computing devices we have today. The result is that on a work site the eye and brain together have a capability that has not yet technically been equalled in any other way."

The likelihood is that by the 21st century man will leave his vehicles and take up residence as a free swimmer on the bottom of the sea. To do this, to take man out of the steel or glass spheres that protect him from the numbing cold, the crushing depths, and the other hazards of an environment at least as hostile as the moon, will require enormous technical breakthroughs. A diver is limited to certain depths by his own physiology. The primary requirement is respiration. Men breathe air, a gas composed of twenty per cent oxygen, seventy-five per cent nitrogen, and a few per cent of other gases, and the ocean is liquid, unbreathable—at least for now. As a result, man must carry his air supply with him. Ordinary compressed air, carried in tanks, can be breathed only as far down as two hundred feet. Below this depth, air breathing is impossible because of the great pressures—0.45 pounds per square inch for every foot of depth—which force the nitrogen through cell walls within the body. When a diver is brought to the surface, he must be slowly decompressed or the nitrogen

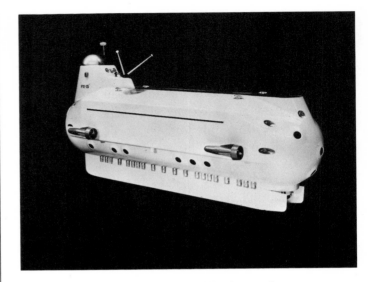

The *PX-15* is a research submersible, designed to carry Dr. Jacques Piccard and a five-man crew on a four-week journey from Florida to Nova Scotia, to study the Gulf Stream at depths of three hundred to twelve hundred feet.

Eventually, the *PX-15* will be used to perform a variety of tasks. Here it becomes a salvage vessel armed with a heavy-duty crane.

will bubble and burst the cells in which it is trapped, causing severe injury and even death. Thus, for every hour spent working at two hundred feet, a diver must spend 199 minutes decompressing at various stages before he can surface.

Nitrogen also causes the so-called rapture of the deep, a narcotic euphoria that causes a man to lose touch with the realities of undersea dangers. Below two hundred feet, gas mixtures are used to replace normal air. Helium, for example, is substituted for nitrogen and mixed with oxygen. Helium is nonnarcotic down to one thousand feet, but divers still must be decompressed. But below one thousand feet helium is compressed almost to the density of water and is thus unusable in a breathing mixture. The Navy has tried substituting neon for helium, but the cost is prohibitive. Neon rates are one hundred dollars a minute.

Between now and the 21st century, one thousand feet may well be the practical diving limit for man, and his major problem will be the inordinate amount of decompression time needed to overcome the effects of working at such great depths. To overcome this limitation, Captain George F. Bond, of the Naval Medical Research Laboratory, developed the idea of intentionally saturating the diver's body fluids and tissues with the breathing mixture for long periods of time, weeks if necessary, a process that would not increase the required decompression time. Dr. Bond proposed a concept of saturation living, keeping the diver in a special bottom habitat or chamber, so that he would live constantly under the same pressure and breathe the same mixture of gases.

The first major test of the Bond thesis was made in July, 1964, in *Sea Lab I*. Here, four men descended to the base of a Texas Tower off Ber-

The geology of the sea bottom will be a primary concern of the *PX-15*. With power drills and related equipment, engineers hope to perform such tasks as investigating soil mechanics and anchoring offshore platforms, at depths of two thousand feet.

Adding a diver-lockout compartment gives the *PX-15* the same transport and work capability of other planned research submersibles.

Artist's concept of underwater complexes, with docking facilities, living quarters, and work and research areas, which eventually will be part of the oceanographic scene.

muda, 193 feet down, for eleven days. Then, Jacques Yves Cousteau, the pioneering French oceanographer, launched his *Conshelf* experiments of saturation living off the coast of France. There is no question as to the increased effectiveness of the saturation living concept. *Sea Lab II* the 1965 experiment was the most ambitious to date. Commander M. Scott Carpenter headed a team of Navy divers 205 feet below the surface. Inside *Sea Lab II* the oxyhelium mixture was pressurized at one hundred pounds per square inch—equal to the water pressure outside and sufficient to keep the sea from rushing in. Thus, the divers could use an open hatchway providing immediate access to the sea floor.

In all there were three teams of divers, each one staying on the bottom for fifteen days. A full and regular work schedule was maintained beneath the sea. The surrounding waters were explored, and temperatures recorded over a range of forty-eight to fifty-two degrees Fahrenheit. An underwater weather station was set up, the sea bottom mapped, and a rough census made of the fish and other marine creatures who passed and paused curiously to investigate, if only briefly, the strange invader.

Constant physiological studies were made of the men at the bottom to determine the effects of the oxyhelium mix they were breathing and the pressure on their bodies. The most immediate and noticeable effect was on communication. Helium makes everyone sound like Donald Duck, and understanding the so-called helium speech is extremely difficult.

Instruments to unscramble the helium voice have been built, but none has yet proved very successful. Dr. Bond suggests that "until we rebuild the human a little more, why we'll have troubles." "Our approach," say Jacques Cousteau, "is slightly different. We think that we can have an injector of gas in the throat and allow men to speak in an exhaust mask. But that's one approach. The second thing is that instead of trying to correct the voice we are working now in another direction, to design another language that works in helium; that's perfectly feasible. The "e" sound doesn't work, well fine, let's abandon that and find other words because," as Cousteau wryly remarks, "a lot of divers do not have much more than six hundred words in their common language. And we can get them to use a kind of underwater Esperanto."

An artist's sketch of a two-mile-deep undersea community. The sphere would house the crew and serve as the control center for underwater vehicles that would gather samples, drill, and explore the depths. To the left of the sphere is the power plant, an underwater nuclear reactor that would produce three thousand kilowatts of electricity. (*Westinghouse*)

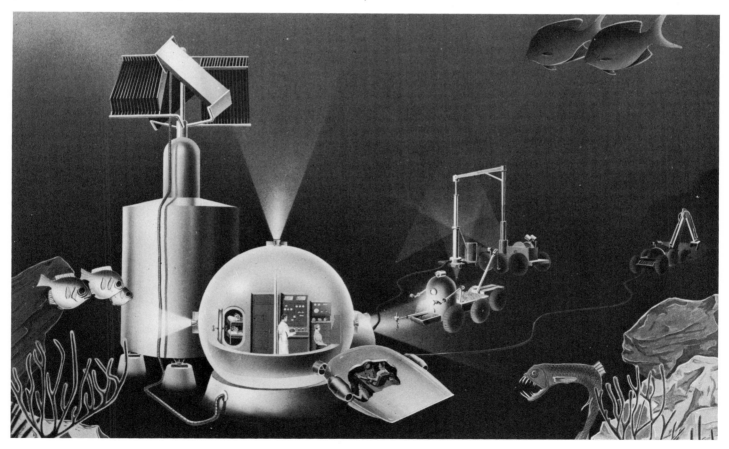

An even greater problem than understanding helium speech is the lack of underwater visibility. At 200 feet or more visibility is extremely poor in most of the world's seas. One answer to the problem may be in the development of lightweight, portable sonar devices. Such hand-held instruments are already in use, and there are plans to harness the unique powers of the laser to illuminate undersea objects. But the major problem for man living in the sea is still depth. "We are now playing at three hundred feet of depth," Dr. George Bond told a recent conference, "and when we step off of three hundred feet, we step out of the present and we step a whole order of magnitude into the future. The other night I sat down and made a list of all of the equipment which we would wish to put on a diver working at a very hostile environment of six hundred feet. I say what we will wish, not what the diver will tolerate. This came up to a total of seventy-six items that we would like to put on this diver at six hundred feet to insure his safety, his workability and so on. Out of those seventy-six items, if I looked on the shelf today, to procure them, exactly four items would be available: his facemask, his weight belt, his knife and his flippers; that's all."

But more and more rapidly the problems of underwater living are yielding to technology. Bond's saturated-living concept, for example, enabled Scott Carpenter to stay underwater for thirty days, yet it demanded no decompression penalty. Carpenter spent only thirty-three hours in a decompression chamber, the same thirty-three hours called for had he stayed eight hours and not thirty days at 205 feet below the surface.

Between now and the beginning of the 21st century man will probe deeper into the oceans.

Much of the underwater work would be accomplished by robot arms or manipulators attached to a small submersible, such as those shown in the drawing attached. (*Autonetics Division, North American Rockwell*)

Mineral maps of the ocean bottom might be made by submarines using ultrasensitive magnetometers, which would sense mineral and petroleum deposits by measuring deviations in the earth's magnetic field. (*The Martin Company*)

Current limitations—for example, the limited capacity of the diver to carry on his back the breathing mix—will be swiftly overcome. At present this is a two-hour supply, and so the diver is dependent upon hoses that tie him to an underwater storage supply and limit severely his mobility and range. This problem may be solved by a closed or semi-closed breathing bag that will free divers of supply lines to habitats and allow them to carry enough oxyhelium with them for extended periods. The Westinghouse Corporation has designed a partially closed system that recycles helium and oxygen and scrubs the carbon dioxide produced in breathing, dumping only every fifth breath into the sea.

A slightly different approach being explored by Westinghouse and Ocean Systems, Inc., is a closed-bag system that recycles the helium while using lithium hydroxide to scrub the carbon dioxide and thus produce oxygen. An integral part of the closed-bag system is an oxygen sensor, a device that will measure the amount of oxygen entering the diver's lungs. The amount varies with depth, so the sensor is an important step forward in deep diving, for it allows divers and shipboard controllers to know exactly how much oxygen they are receiving. This is an important safety advance, for without the sensor a man can black out before he is aware of the fact that he is not getting enough oxygen.

The next step is a feedback control that will not only monitor the amount of oxygen entering the lungs but will also serve as a regulatory system for the amount of the oxygen in the mix.

Beyond the closed-bag systems is a gas-exchange system for bottom habitats being developed by Dr. Harold P. Vind at the Navy's Civil Engineering Laboratory at Port Hueneme, California. Vind's

This diver wears a self-contained underwater breathing rig that recirculates a mixture of gases, thus extending the bottom time. The scuba gear contains a scrubber cannister that removes carbon dioxide and allows the gas to be reused. (*Westinghouse*)

131

system circulates oxygen-depleted air into a gas-exchange tank, where it is flushed by a constantly circulating stream of sea water. Carbon dioxide in the stale air passes into the sea water while oxygen in the water diffuses into the stale air. Then, the now reoxygenated air is returned to a sealed chamber for breathing, while the waste sea water is pumped back into the ocean.

Dr. Vind thinks that the system is best adapted to the shallow depths, where the pressures are low, but the development of a pressure-reducing pump, now underway, will provide the system with a constant and economical flow of water no matter what the undersea pressure. With the addition of the pressure-reducing pump, the system might be used to maintain 21st-century habitats at atmospheric pressure at almost any depth.

The water-scrubbed air system is a major step forward, but it does not completely free man from his need for some umbilical tie to the surface. The original fresh air that must be pumped into the system must come from the surface. What is needed is a gill, an artificial mechanism that will take the oxygen man needs for respiration directly from the sea water. One means of doing this is a membranous film of silicone rubber that acts like a suspicious border guard. It permits oxygen to pass from sea water into the air in one direction and carbon dioxide to pass the other way, from the air into the water. This selectivity is a result of the solubility and diffusion characteristics of the film. A molecule of oxygen in sea water dissolves into the membrane, is carried through, and emerges into the air environment as a gas molecule of oxygen. The same effect, in reverse, is produced with carbon-dioxide molecules that pass from the air into the sea. The General Electric Company,

Artist's concept of a project, called Bottom Fix, in which modular units are anchored in clusters, as needed, to provide working and living complexes anywhere underwater. *(General Electric)*

which is experimenting with this membrane, has called it a Permselective Membrane. GE envisions the day when the walls of underwater habitats might be made of Permselective Membranes, suitably braced, which would not only hold back the sea but filch oxygen from it and return carbon dioxide to it. Already, they have kept a number of mammals—rabbits, cats, rats—alive in submerged chambers with the only air supply that which passes through the membrane.

Materials such as the Permselective Membrane might one day provide the basis for a set of artificial gills for man. Says Harris Stewart, Director of the Commerce Department's Oceanographic Institute: "We have artificial lungs. We have artificial eyes, hearing aids, a lot of us have artificial teeth. Why not artificial gills with a little switch so that you could switch from using your lungs to using your gills?"

In an ocean that is eighty-six per cent dissolved oxygen, the Permselective Membrane makes such a question answerable. There may perhaps be no need to outfit man with gills. It might, by the 21st century, be possible for man to actually breathe water and extract from it the oxygen he needs without the intervention of artificial devices. In a few laboratories attempts are being made to extract oxygen from fluids in the lungs themselves. Oxygenated fluorocarbons, salt water, and silicone oils in the lungs of mice, rats, and cats have enabled them to "breathe" underwater for periods of up to twenty hours. None of the animals yet tested has survived the return to air breathing with any great success. Mice, however, seem to recover from breathing fluorocarbon liquids—an industrial lubricating fluid—after being submerged for up to eight hours. The mechanism seems relatively simple. Oxygen is at least ten times as soluble in silicone and fluorochemical liquids as it is in blood plasma and salt water. Thus, a given volume of oxygen-saturated fluorocarbon contains three times as much oxygen as the same volume of air, blood, or sea water. Although oxygenated fluorocarbons have given the best results so far, they are not sea water. An additional problem is that a man's lungs, which have a surface area as large as a tennis court, may still be too small to extract the required oxygen from a liquid. But the mere fact that liquid breathing is at least theoretically possible and experimentally proven means that the depths to which man may one day dive are limited only by the physiological border of the body itself. Captain George Bond, head of the Navy's Man-In-The-Sea Program, has already postulated the idea of filling a diver's lungs with a circulating oxygenated liquid and flooding his head sinus cavities to protect the diver from pressures as extreme as those found as far down as 12,000 feet.

Whatever the mechanism—a liquid breathing Permselective Membrane, the conventional compressed-air tank, or the special oxyhelium mix—man will explore the deep ocean—the last frontier left on his earth. By the 21st century, it too may have been tamed to the point where we look upon it as simply another resource, abused, polluted, and taken for granted. But perhaps not. Never before in his history has man taken on anything quite so immense as the sea, the enormous powers it generates, and the great, seemingly inexhaustible life that teems within it.

"Within fifty years," says Dr. Fred N. Spiess, Assistant Director of the Scripps Oceanographic Institute in La Jolla, California, "man will move onto and into the sea, occupying it and exploiting it as an integral part of his use of this planet for recreation, minerals, food, waste disposal, military and transportation operations, and, as populations grow, for actual living space."

In tapping the riches of the sea, we may not have the leisurely span of fifty years at our disposal. The pressure of half a world filled with hunger and malnutrition may demand that we attack the sea for its protein almost immediately. The sea is a potential source of food so vast as to baffle even the experts as to its true contents. The reason for this happy confusion lies in the very nature of life on earth. Virtually all food (and all food originates as life in some form) begins in the form of stored sunlight in plants. Through the chemical miracle of photosynthesis, the sun's energy is converted into the chemical nutrients needed to support plant life, which in turn provides food for animal life. But most of the earth—seventy per cent of it—is covered by water, and as a result, more solar energy is converted to food in the watery sea than on the dry land.

"Water," explains Wilbert Chapman, Director of Resources of the Van Camp Sea Food Company, "is a perfect solvent for the inorganic materials plants use as nutrients. The rains of aeons have been washing them from the land to the depths of the ocean, until the ocean has become a virtual bank of the world's fertility. Massive ocean currents boil continuous fountains of mineral nutrients up into the sunlight near the surface and, as a result, nearly every drop of ocean water to a depth of one hundred feet supports plant life, a growth vastly greater than the total production of plant life on land."

The actual process begins in microscopic plants known as diatoms, which trap the sun's rays and

Artist's concept of an automated ocean convoy for overseas transportation of bulk cargo. Orbiting satellites provide the navigation instructions for pilotless tugs, hauling plastic cargo cocoons to a rendezvous point, where human pilots then board and guide them to the docking facilities. *(The Martin Company)*

135

use them to produce droplets of oil. The diatoms are part of a vast network of microorganisms, both plant and animal, that compose the most numerous class of life in the sea—plankton. It is estimated that each year, the ocean produces between four hundred and seven hundred billion metric tons of plankton—enough to turn miles of sea into vast heaving meadows of red, green, or orange. Yet for all its profligate abundance, plankton is not worth the cost and energy it takes to harvest. But plankton that has been converted into usable protein by the fish that feed on it can solve the world's hunger problems.

"When people talk about the sea as a source of protein food for people, animal protein food, the estimates are just wild," says Athelstan Spilhaus. "Nobody agrees, not even scientists agree, but the confusion occurs because sometimes one man is thinking of the conventional fish that we eat, the haddock, or the tuna, or the salmon, and these fish are carnivorous fish who eat littler fish and furthermore, they eat little fish who have eaten littler fish and those third-stage little fish have eaten the plankton, so that there have been four conversions. Really the energy of protein comes from the sunshine through the green plants, and if you can eat the anchovies and the sardines that are grazing fish and eat the green plants, then you get the maximum amount of protein from the sea, so that I would be almost certain that by the year 2000, we will have been able to find ways of getting the necessary texture and taste to these lower-trophic-level grazing fish and we'll be eating them and the carnivorous fish will be considered as predators on our pastures in the sea. They'll be like the wolves, lions and tigers that you keep away from eating your cattle."

The increasing sophistication of our oceanographic research is for the first time revealing intimate glimpses of the life in the sea in all its myriad forms. This spiny creature, a channel rockfish, was photographed from a diving saucer nine hundred feet beneath the surface in the La Jolla submarine canyon. *(Scripps Institution of Oceanography)*

At the bottom of a thousand-foot canyon, the camera uncovers a reddish-colored spiny spider crab stalking a canyon ledge. *(Scripps Institution of Oceanography)*

At the moment we are eating the game fish, the lions and wolves of the sea, and getting very little in the way of an efficient protein return. The actual figures are rather discouraging in terms of the wastefulness of energy, but the food chain works in this manner: ten thousand pounds of plant plankton provide food for only one thousand pounds of animal plankton, such as small shrimp. Sardines, anchovies, menhaden, and hake—the so-called trash fish—gorge themselves on one thousand pounds of planktonic shrimp and convert it into a mere one hundred pounds of trash fish muscle. Tuna, the tiger of the sea, will hunt down and devour one hundred pounds of trash fish in order to turn it into ten pounds of tuna protein. If a man eats ten pounds of tuna, he will end up with only one additional pound of human protein. This then is the incredibly wasteful trophic chain— a massive ten thousand pounds of plant plankton required at its start to make up one pound of human protein at its end. But there is an extraordinarily simple way of increasing the efficiency of protein conversion. Man must learn to take his bites far lower down on the food chain. He must draw his protein not from the game fish such as tuna at the end but from the trash fish, the menhaden and hake, closer to the start of things.

This can be done by the use of a powder called fish protein concentrate, or FPC, which is a tasteless, odorless powder. It is made by grinding up trash fish—the entire fish, scales, bones, head— into powder and then drying it in huge ovens. FPC can solve the world's protein problem, a problem so vast that one hundred million people each year contract kwashiorkor, a protein deficiency disease that sickens, deteriorates, and finally kills. In all, some two billion people are

137

thought to suffer today from protein malnutrition of some sort.

The problem could be solved completely by the addition of ten grams of FPC mixed into every protein-deficient daily diet. The cost is estimated at two dollars per person a year. We now catch some fifty million metric tons of fish a year. An additional seven million tons converted directly to FPC would solve the protein malnutrition problems of today's world. By the year 2001, however, the world's population may have doubled to seven billion, or ballooned even more. A correspondingly greater fish catch will be required to provide the protein supplement needed for a hungry world. To accomplish this, we shall have to improve radically our methods of fishing, which today are, by contrast to our agricultural methods, incredibly primitive.

"We will eventually go to ranching in the oceans," declares Scripps oceanographer John Isaacs. "Ranching in this parlance is sending out a preferred herbivore, one feeding as far down in the trophic level as possible, to range. We will use his energy, which he derives continuously from the environment, to reap this thin crop and to bring it back to us in the form of animal protein. It's precisely analogous to ranching in general."

The problem, however, is to get the fish to bring his protein back to us. One approach to solving that problem, in effect, the problem of transforming man from a primitive hunter of the seas to a rancher, is under development in Japan. At the Yashima Station on the Inland Sea, Dr. Harato calls fish to a specific site by the use of Pavlovian conditioning. The basis of the technique is Pavlov's earlier experiments with dogs, in which a bell was rung just before the dogs were fed. After feeding

Dr. John Isaacs of the Scripps Institution of Oceanography. *(Scripps Institution of Oceanography)*

138

had been paired many times with the ringing bell, the sound of the bell alone was sufficient to start them salivating. The fish are raised from larvae in tanks, and every time they are fed, a buzzer sounds. Dr. Harato hopes that when the fish grow older and are released into the sea, the same buzzer will reach them and summon them to the table.

When the fish are large enough to leave their tanks for the bay, the conditioning is continued. An automatic feeder whirls about, tossing out food like a man seeding a lawn, to the accompaniment of the buzzer. Still later, the fish are released from the confined bay into the ocean. For six or nine months they are free to graze on the natural pastures of the sea. But there comes a day when the fishing boats come, sound their buzzers, and wait for the fish to swim to the source of the noise for food, as they did when they were young. But instead of finding food, they are scooped up by a fisherman's net.

Eventually, as our knowledge of fish genetics increases, we may be able to build spawning instincts like those of salmon into the fish. They might then be raised in estuaries, sent out to sea to graze and when the biological urge to spawn occurs, brought back to the estuaries where they were raised. Harvesting fish will then be a simple matter.

In the years between now and the 21st century, however, hunting will still be a major means of getting fish. To improve hunting methods, techniques are being developed to predict the appearance of fish in certain areas of the ocean at a specific time. The Tuna Resources Laboratory of the Bureau of Commercial Fisheries is predicting the location of tuna in the Pacific. Using computers to assess certain physical characteristics of the sea that vary with time—currents, temperatures, salinity, the amounts of dissolved oxygen and nutrients present—the scientists note interactions between these characteristics and the fish presence and produce weekly charts to show where the fish are and where they are most likely to be in the near future. Fish locations can now be predicted with great accuracy up to fifteen days in advance, and by the 21st century predictions of two and three months in advance will be possible.

Much of the technological development needed to aid fish catching is dependent upon our first learning far more than we know now about the life cycles and habits of fish. A study of the trophic chain has shown that fish are where the food is and at the same level on which it is found—near the surface, at the bottom, or in the middle depths. Most fish are found within a range of the surface and a depth of two hundred feet, which is the depth to which sunlight penetrates and, consequently, the deepest point at which plankton grows. But some fish scavenge the bottom where the larvae of small fish and crustaceans are generally deposited. The predators, however, are most often found ranging the trophic level for the small fish that follow the plankton up and down the depths in response to the movement of the sun.

In the open sea, where the bottom is hundreds of fathoms deep, life concentrates near the surface and around seamounts and shipwrecks, the latter serving as floating landmarks in the sea.

Fish also mass about broad currents and great upwelling streams of ocean that bubble from bottom fissures and carry the nutrients needed to spark a trophic chain. The Humboldt Current off the coast of Peru intersects just such a great upwelling, and a great anchovy fishery has been founded at the confluence. Fish are sensitive to odors, sound waves, and obstructions in their path. They are, like moths, attracted to light and have an affinity for the positive pole of an electrical current.

Much of this knowledge and the far greater details to be added by research will be applied to the increasingly important task of catching fish. One experimental approach that may become a commonplace by the 21st century is the use of plastic platforms that float on the surface to attract huge schools of fish by serving as landmarks. Twenty-first-century fishing trawlers might lay a line hundreds of miles long with hundreds of attached platforms and simply work their way back along the line, harvesting the fish gathered about the platforms. Specific odors might be released from the platforms as a further lure.

The ultimate in efficient fish catching might be something on the order of this description offered by Dayton Alverson, of the Bureau of Commercial Fisheries: "A net of unmanned buoys has been established for several years in the sea, and the patterns of occurrence and distribution of natural resources have been plotted. The buoys are interrogated at regular intervals through satellite telemetering and from their surface transmitters by pulse-coded sonic means to instrument heads at various depths in the sea. Only points of parameter change are telemetered. As the data comes in to a central data point, computers reduce the mass of informational bits to contoured plots of biological parameters. These are transmitted to fishery centers around the world. When an anomaly occurs, it is metered by the buoy, sent to the center, and analyzed, and so the movement of identified resources would be plotted. The nature of the anomaly would be checked by aircraft equipped with laserscopes. Depending on the species identified, the main fleet could be deployed into the path of the fish, or conversely suitable deterrents could be placed in the sea to guide the fish to the catcher. Aircraft could disperse the necessary chemical pellets to olfactorily guide the fish, or remote-controlled underwater vehicles would produce the necessary electrical, sonic, or bubble barrier to perform the same function. Depending on the depth of the harvest, catches would be performed by catcher boats assigned to permanently anchored factory ships or by automated underwater vehicles operated from ship or shore stations."

Thus might man be converted from hunter to rancher of the seas in the 21st century. But despite all his new technologies, man's greatest asset in the sea may be the *Tursiops truncatus*, the bottle-nosed porpoise. The intelligence and abilities of the porpoise have been explored and written about for quite some time now, and it is, therefore, not at all improbable to envision the porpoise herding fish in some underwater roundup.

Today, as we are training men to work beneath the sea, we are also training porpoises to work with them. At the moment our goals are modest. Porpoises respond to diver's signals, fetch and carry, and act much like well-trained dogs. Just how far the porpoise will go in assisting man is an open question. It has displayed an extraordinary affinity for man, perhaps because it too is a mammal and once lived on the land before returning to the sea millions of years ago. As a swimmer, the porpoise can reach speeds of twenty-five knots, faster than most ships. His brain is larger than man's, and efforts to communicate with him have been moderately successful. By the 21st century,

This porpoise, at Sea Life Park in Hawaii, obeys spoken commands to swim forward, to jump through a hoop, or to stop in mid-swim and break off a maneuver.

Porpoises may one day serve as the foremen of man's undersea domain. Here, in an artist's rendering, they are shown herding schools of fish.

we may have learned his language and he ours. Then he may become the foreman in charge of man's underwater world.

And what a world it will be, a world that will be exploited at a prodigious rate, for within it lies wealth in quantities we can only guess at. It will unquestionably answer our protein needs for centuries to come, but after food, man's major need is for power.

One hope for the 21st century is to harness somehow the enormous power of the sea itself. For all of his history man has lived in fear of the sea's powers. In the past tidal waves have smashed coastal cities to bits, storm-lashed seas have battered islands and recarved coast lines, swift-moving currents have eroded mountains and cut channels between continents.

The harnessing of this great power is being attempted by the French in their Brittany tidal power plant, which uses the tide to spin electric generators. The deep currents of the oceans are also thought to be a source of limitless power. One expert proposes that we put down underwater generators in the axis of the Gulf Stream. Fifty miles wide and thousands of feet deep, the Gulf Stream is one of the world's greatest sources of power, flowing continuously at a speed of four to six knots. "We could put down with the aid of diver-carrying submarines," suggests Ed Link, "some suspended houses or power stations and then use a system similar to the one we use on the turbines. Funneling this water through the stations with a six-knot stream could generate tremendous quantities of power that would be carried by cables back to land."

Still another approach is to use the thermal gradient—the difference in temperature—of two points in the sea. There is, for example, a significant temperature difference between the Gulf Stream and the waters immediately adjoining it. J. Hilbert Anderson, an engineer, has proposed a scheme whereby warm surface water would boil propane. The vapors produced would then pass through a turbine, expand, and set the turbine spinning. To maintain the cycle, the exhaust would be cooled and condensed by cold water from beneath the surface. Anderson claims that under this system the Gulf Stream alone could supply the United States with one hundred times the power it will need in the year 2001. On a far more modest scale, the Japanese have developed a storage battery that picks up energy from lapping waves, stores it, and uses it to power a light on a buoy.

One of the key resources from which power flows is oil, and the search for it has at last turned seaward. Within the rocks of the world's continental

Huge undersea farms can be cultivated and harvested by automated equipment in fairly shallow depths. The crop would be kelp, a protein-rich seaweed that is already used as a food supplement for cattle in some countries and as a vegetable delicacy in others.

shelves there may be locked about two and a half trillion barrels of oil. To tap this incredible source of petroleum reserves, huge floating drills—some half the size of the *Queen Mary*—are being towed to the site of the North Sea oil discovery for use when the off-shore drilling begins. In 1966 sixteen per cent of all the oil produced in the world came from beneath the sea. And the gas and oil strikes in the North Sea may one day provide more oil than now comes from the Middle East. One projection is that by 1975 forty per cent of the western world's oil may be supplied by under-water sources.

The key to increased oil and gas production in the sea is the development of new tools to make ocean mining profitable. Finding and sinking an oil well at sea costs between eight and twenty times as much as it does on dry land, but these costs are coming down as new methods and tools are developed. One major problem is the weather on the surface. A bad blow can destroy a floating rig, a modest wind can halt all operations as waves toss the rig up and down like a yo-yo. One major engineering aim is to develop equipment and techniques to take men to the bottom of the sea where they can work beyond reach of the weather. One such system already in use is called Cachalot, after a deep-diving whale. Designed by Westinghouse, Cachalot consists of a surface chamber and an elevator that carries men to a work site on the bottom. Like the *Sea Lab*, Cachalot employs the saturated-living concept, and so both chamber and elevator are filled with breathing gases and pressurized to the depth of the work site. Thus, the men can work on the bottom for hours and instead of decompressing, return to the surface chamber, where the same pressure is maintained. The next

This Cachalot rig, named for a deep-diving whale, is anchored over a work site. It has saturated living quarters that enable the divers to work underwater for days at a time. *(Westinghouse)*

day they descend again to the work site and need not decompress until the job—lasting for days or even weeks—is finished. In actual practice, Westinghouse engineers have found it more practical to use two crews on the same job, so that while one crew works on the bottom and lives in the pressurized chamber, the second crew decompresses and is off for a week. Eventually, a 21st-century oil field on the ocean bottom may pipe oil from its wells directly into submarine tankers or pipelines that feed from the wells into shore-based refineries.

Still another approach is to build structures on the surface capable of withstanding severe storms. Just off the coast of Long Beach, California, a number of man-made islands are being built to pump oil from the bottom of the bay. A consortium of Texaco, Humble, Union, Mobil, and Shell—THUMS—is doing the work and have agreed to landscape the islands so as not to disturb the view from the beach.

The man-made island idea is not new. The Japanese have been mining iron ore from Tokyo Bay and using the waste materials to construct the islands since 1960. A steel island, the largest ever built by man, now sits seven miles off Grand Isle, Louisiana, atop a huge salt dome in the Gulf of Mexico.

The true extent of the mineral wealth in the sea is virtually incalculable. Some oceanographers have estimated that the sea contains some fifty million million metric tons of minerals. Included in this staggering figure are two million million tons of magnesium, one hundred thousand million tons of bromine, seven hundred thousand million tons of boron, twenty billion tons of uranium, fifteen billion tons of copper, fifteen billion tons of manganese, five hundred million tons of silver, and ten million tons of gold.

Even with present-day technologies, which fall far short of the challenges posed by the sea, an enormous ocean-mining industry is developing. Using slant mines that tunnel from the land outward and down sixty feet beneath the bay, the Japanese are extracting thirteen million tons of coal every year. The continental shelves are being mined for their tin off Thailand, their diamonds off the coast of South Africa, where the yield is five carats per ton, five times as much as is found on land. In the Gulf of Mexico, in Faxa Bay in Iceland, and off the coast of the Carolinas, calcareous shell deposits are mined to provide calcium carbonate for cement and other industrial purposes. In Faxa Bay alone the rate of shell formation far exceeds the rate of extraction.

Off the western coasts of most continents, wind, the rotation of the earth, and the shape of the continental slopes combine to funnel the surface waters offshore. Deep water rises to replace it, and these upwelling seas carry tricalcium phosphate to the surface, where it undergoes a chemical change and becomes phosphorite, which is deposited back on the bottom as nodules or coatings on rocks. Phosphorite is an important fertilizer, consumed at the rate of thirty million tons a year. The phosphorite deposit off the coast of California alone contains one and a half billion tons.

At the moment, the production of most of these minerals is simply too expensive for them to compete with land sources of the same materials, but the cost is coming down rapidly. Dr. John Mero, a leading authority on undersea mining, says: "It would be profitable to mine materials such as phosphate, nickel, copper, cobalt, and even manganese from the sea at today's costs and prices.

"And I firmly believe that within the next generation, the sea will be a major source not only of those metals but of molybdenum, vanadium, lead, zinc, titanium, zirconium, and several other metals."

One means of reducing the cost is to combine a variety of functions within a complex of operations. Much of our lime, for example, comes from oyster shells that sit in gigantic mounds in the Gulf of Mexico. Barges haul these shells into a chemical plant at Freeport, Texas, where they are burned to get the lime. The lime is then used to extract magnesium that is dissolved in sea water. The yield is one pound of magnesium from every 142 gallons of sea water. The sea water could then be sent on through another process to extract its bromine, sodium, calcium, potassium, and boron, all of which are dissolved in sea water in high concentrations. This would not be the end of the chain, however, for the process of removal would have done much to desalt the water, and a final desalinization process would produce fresh water. The salty wastes that remained might be used as a pond in which to grow brine shrimp, and thus add to the world's food supply.

The process of extracting minerals from sea water is under careful study in a number of countries, and one method in particular looks very promising. This is an ion-exchange technique that enables molecules carrying different electrical charges to exchange places on either side of a membrane being developed by Britain's National Physical Laboratory. Scientists there have found a resin that is particularly adept at separating uranium from sea water by ion exchange. Now

Scientists on an expedition to the Gulf of Alaska examine a haul of rock samples, dredged up from the ocean floor more than a mile beneath the ship. *(Scripps Institution of Oceanography)*

148

they are looking for resins that will do the same thing for other metals in solution. The result, when found, might be sea-borne refineries that would cruise the oceans, straining valuable metals from the waters on which they float. Dr. John Mero suggests anchoring porous bags of these resins in areas of high current flow or towing them behind merchant ships to get valuable raw materials at an extremely low cost.

The extraction of minerals in solution appears to be an easier task than actually mining the ocean bottom. We have known for almost a hundred years now that the deep sea floor is carpeted with valuable minerals simply waiting to be scooped up. Manganese nodules, for example, litter the floors of most oceans. The Pacific alone contains some one and a half trillion tons, and the stockpile is added to as more nodules form at the rate of another ten million tons a year. Looking like overgrown pebbles, an inch to a foot in diameter, the nodules lie on the surface of the sea-floor sediments in concentrations as high as 100,000 tons per square mile. The nodules are not pure manganese but contain an average of two and a half per cent copper, two per cent nickel, one and a third per cent cobalt, and thirty-six per cent manganese.

Still another approach to making ocean mining economically feasible may come from basic research into the methods by which nature concentrates minerals into nodules at the sea bottom. It now appears that the minerals may be concentrated by aquatic animals and plants that act as nitrogen-fixing bacteria do on land to "fix" metals into concentration on the bottom. Like oysters, small animals and plants take sea water into their bodies and squirt it out another aperture, in the process separating a particular mineral or minerals from the water and concentrating it around a small central grain of sand.

Some scientists hope that after sufficient study these organisms might be cultivated in estuaries with high tides that circulate sea water. In this manner they might act as a living extraction plant, concentrating metals where we can get at them easily.

Other minerals such as aluminum and copper are buried in red clays that cover one hundred million square kilometers of ocean floor. Neither the nodules nor the clays have yet been touched, but as the rich nations of the world exhaust their land resources and the poor nations struggle toward industrialization, the demand for raw materials will be enormous.

What happens then when all of Africa reaches the material level of 1969 America by 2001? The simple problem of equipping that giant continent with a telephone system equivalent to that of the United States today would call for a mountain of copper wire that would exceed the world's land-based supply. To satisfy these needs, we must, between now and the beginning of the 21st century, develop the methods and the tools to take from the sea the materials we shall need to live on the land.

7

The Search for Yesterday

The numbers that must be used to describe the universe are almost beyond our comprehension. For example, our sun is a star, one of perhaps a hundred billion, in a galaxy we call the Milky Way. The Milky Way in turn is but one of billions of galaxies. And new stars and galaxies are continuously being formed. It is almost as if a 21st-century mind were needed to encompass it all. And the question raised by the mere mechanics of this vastness might occupy the minds of men forever.

For some, it is enough to say simply that God created it all. For the scientist this answer is not adequate. The creation, the scientist believes, followed verifiable physical laws. "I cannot believe God played dice with the universe," declared Albert Einstein.

In the 21st century we may learn the answers, but they will come from the work being done in cosmology today. The jumping-off point for today's speculations is a controversial theory of a Belgian priest, Abbé Georges Lemaître. In the 1920s astronomers found that most of the observable galaxies seemed to be rushing away from each other at great speeds. To account for this observation, Lemaître declared that it was the result of the creation of the universe.

"In the beginning," said the scientist-priest, "there was simply a ball of primordial matter. Within this ball was all of the matter in the universe and it was packed very densely. The density caused great heat to build up inside the ball or 'cosmic egg' and finally it exploded. It was the most enormous, cataclysmic explosion that could be imagined, and the pieces that were thrown outward eventually formed the galaxies. The present headlong flight of the galaxies away from one

Sir Bernard Lovell, director of the Jodrell Bank Observatory and one of the world's leading astronomers.

another, which we see today, is the result of this original explosion. Astronomers call this theory of creation the 'big bang.' "

Other theories have also been presented and supported by scientists in the last thirty years, but astronomy's newest tools—the space vehicle and the radio telescope—have gathered some evidence that seems to rule out these other theories, leaving the big bang as the most likely possibility. But the theory is not complete, and variations of it are multiple. Now, however, we have the proper tools to reach out into the recesses of space and ferret out answers that were previously hidden.

Says astronomer Sir Bernard Lovell, Director of England's Jodrell Bank Radio Astronomy Observatory, "It's an extraordinary thing that we have this great good fortune of living in an age which is witness to development of these two techniques, the space probe and the radio telescope. And each of these is having the same kind of impact on astronomy that the uses of the telescope by Galileo three and a half centuries ago had."

One space probe launched from the White Sands Missile Range carried a scanner capable of detecting X-rays in space. In the last few years about ten extremely powerful X-ray sources have been located by rocket sightings. All have been in our own galactic neighborhood, that is, within the Milky Way galaxy. Powerful as the X-rays are, they cannot penetrate the earth's atmosphere and thus are not detectable from terrestrial observatories. But the excitement engendered by their discovery must rank with that of Galileo's when he first saw the cratered face of the moon leap into magnified focus through his crude telescope. For these X-ray sources have opened up an entirely

Among the newest of astronomy's tools is the radio
telescope. One of the largest is this 250-foot, steerable
parabolic reflector at the Jodrell Bank Observatory in
England.

new age of astronomy, have, in fact, created the new discipline known as X-ray astronomy.

The scanner-carrying rocket located what may be a stellar birth taking place in a constellation called Scorpius, some forty billion miles from the earth. But a star not yet fully formed will remain invisible to ordinary telescopes for several million years. The importance of the new field of X-ray astronomy cannot be challenged, for it will enable scientists to locate stars in the formative process. Thus, we gain a bit more insight into the origin of all things.

This insight comes primarily through the measurements made by the scanner, which showed that the X-rays boiling forth from Scorpius were confined to a region less than twenty seconds of arc in width. Other measurements placed the source practically in our backyard, a scant thirty thousand light years away. The two parameters—narrow width and relative proximity—indicated to scientists that the source of the X-rays was a rather small object, as cosmic objects go. At this point in time the X-ray source is larger than our entire solar system, but it is far less dense and thus at a much earlier stage than that in which planets begin to form within the disc-shaped cloud surrounding a newly forming star.

What is probably happening is that the gases within the cloud are condensing. Turbulence whips the molecules about, crashing them into one another, pulling the cloud closer together into a tight ball of whirling, tumbling, agitated atoms. The ball will grow denser, increasing the gravitational pull toward the center. The contraction will continue, building up enormous temperatures in the interior of the ball. At twenty million degrees Fahrenheit hydrogen atoms stripped of their electrons fuse together to form a deuteron, a nucleus of heavy hydrogen, and the fusion process continues until helium nuclei are formed in a cosmic birth trauma that starts a massive thermonuclear furnace to power the newborn star.

The X-ray star we are now watching is not yet at the point of thermonuclear delivery. It will probably not become dense enough to be observed with an optical telescope for at least another million years.

Not nearly so immature, but still quite young as stars are counted, is our own sun. It is perhaps five billion years old, and its thermonuclear furnace can be expected to maintain this so-called main sequence of its life span for another five to ten billion years. During this time the temperature in a star's core builds up from twenty million degrees centigrade, when hydrogen first begins to fuse, to a hundred million degrees centigrade, when three helium nuclei can combine to yield carbon. At seven hundred million degrees the carbon nuclei react with themselves, generating sodium and neon. The first signs of age show when the star begins to swell its borders, becoming grossly distended to up to one hundred times its previous size, and then takes on a reddish tinge. It has become a red giant. When the thermonuclear reactions have consumed all of the hydrogen and other light elements, the star may begin to collapse upon itself with astonishing rapidity. Then suddenly it explodes and becomes a supernova, the final fiery death throes of a star. During this explosion, the heavier elements are molded and shot out into space to form the cosmic seeds for a new generation of stars.

Few stars die in so spectacular a fashion. Most simply exhaust their fuel and grow incredibly

Fiery gases pour out from the sun in this photograph, taken with coronograph instruments carried aloft by rocket. A coronograph creates an artificial eclipse of the sun to permit study of solar flares. *(Naval Research Laboratory)*

dense until a thimbleful of matter taken from one of these so-called white dwarfs would weigh several tons. But during its life cycle, when the thermonuclear heart pulses, the enormous energies generated are radiated in the form of heat and light. And there are other forms of radiation given off—X-rays, gamma rays, and radio waves.

The radio waves stars give off are captured and studied at astronomical observatories such as Jodrell Bank in England. "With the radio telescope," explains Sir Bernard Lovell, "we are penetrating so far into space that we're studying the epochs of time which take us back many thousands of millions of years, and we're studying the universe not as it is now, at this moment, but as it was in regions of time where it was possibly in an entirely different state, where it may have been closer to its early condition or evolution in origin."

To an astronomer, this means that the light reaching us today from stars that are billions of miles away is light that was radiated billions of years ago. Thus, when we look at very distant galaxies, we are seeing the universe as it was billions of years ago.

But only a small fraction of the light given off by all the stars reaches us. Some stars are so far away that their light simply never reaches us with enough intensity to be detected. Radio waves move at the same speed as light waves, but are much longer and, therefore, can pass through interstellar dust and gas that are opaque to light. Thus, radio telescopes can peer out farther than the more familiar optical telescopes.

Most radio sources are powerful and seem to come from whole galaxies rather than individual stars. The farther away they are, the more difficult

Dr. Alan Sandage of Mount Palomar Observatory, where 3C-273 was identified optically for the first time with the two-hundred-inch telescope.

The first quasi-stellar radio source to be photographed was 3C-273, seen at center. *(California Institute of Technology)*

it becomes to pinpoint the precise location of an individual radio star. But the general locations of more than one hundred of these radio sources have been found and logged in a special catalogue compiled at Cambridge University in England. Within the last few years, radio sources labeled 3C-48, 3C-147, 3C-273, and others in the "Third Cambridge Catalogue of Radio Stars" were getting considerable attention. An intense effort was begun to uncover the stars that were thought to be sending forth the 3C radio waves. One part of the effort involved the unsuccessful use of the giant two-hundred-inch telescope at Mount Palomar in California, the largest optical telescope in the world. But in Australia, astronomer Cyril Hazard kept his radio telescope aimed at a radio source known as 3C-273 and each night the moon, in its plodding orbit about the earth, moved closer to the imaginary line that could be drawn between 3C-273 and Hazard's telescope. Then, as the moon moved in front of 3C-273, its radio waves were abruptly cut off. At that instant, the edge of the moon was slicing like a compass arc across the exact location of 3C-273.

The directional information was passed on to Dr. Allan Sandage at the Mount Palomar Observatory so that he could focus the great optical mirror there on that specific region of the sky. For, while the size of optical telescopes limits the amount of light they can gather and thus the distance at which they can detect objects, they do have one advantage. Light waves tell us more about a star than do radio waves alone. And so the great telescope was aligned along the coordinates furnished by Cyril Hazard.

Pictures were taken and examined. The results were hardly exciting, for 3C-273 looked like noth-

157

Dr. Maarten Schmidt, professor of astronomy at the California Institute of Technology and staff member of the Mount Wilson and Palomar Observatories. *(California Institute of Technology)*

ing more than some dim stars in our own galaxy.

It was in fact a relatively dim thirteen-magnitude star in the constellation Virgo and had been known for some seventy years. It had been recorded on photographic sweeps of the sky several times before. But like millions of other ordinary-looking stars, it had never been examined very closely. But to Sandage and Jesse Greenstein, head of the Astronomy Department at the California Institute of Technology, which helps run the Mount Palomar Observatory, it seemed incredible that such a minor star could be pouring out such vast radio energies.

The task of investigation fell to Maarten Schmidt, a young astronomer at the California Institute of Technology. Schmidt began by aiming another instrument—the spectrograph—at the radio source. The spectrograph is a major analytical tool that splits up the composite light from a star into its component colors, in much the same way a prism breaks a sunbeam into a rainbow of individual colors.

The individual wave lengths of starlight appear on a spectrograph as a series of light and dark lines. Each line represents a basic element in the stars. By analyzing the position of each line, the astronomer can determine what elements a star contains, for each element emits or absorbs radiation of certain frequencies, each with its own characteristic position on the spectrum.

The spectrograph can provide other clues of extreme importance. One is the velocity in the line of sight with which a star is moving. When a star is receding from the earth, the light received from it seems to be lower in frequency, just as the whistle of a freight train seems to decrease in pitch as the train pulls away from the station. The influence of the motion of the source on the sound or light it emits is called the Doppler effect. Each line on the spectrograph of receding stars shifts from its normal position toward the red end of the spectrum. It was a red shift of galaxies observed with the spectrographs that led Dr. Edwin Hubble in 1922 to conclude that all of the galaxies were rushing away from each other. Were a galaxy to be moving toward us, then its spectrograph would display a violet shift. The distance on the spectrograph that a line is shifted from its normal position toward either the violet or red end of the spectrum can tell us how fast the object is moving in the line of sight and thus how far away it is.

Lemaître's big-bang theory is based on the fact that almost all of the galaxies in the universe show red shifts. And the farther away from us they are, the fainter their light and the greater the red shifts. This phenomenon was the basis for Hubble's general law that the farther the galaxy, the greater its speed of recession.

But how did 3C-273 fit into all this? Photographically, it was a faint star that seemed totally undistinguished. But its spectrum was startling. "If you thought of a 3C-273 as being a member of our own galaxy," Schmidt says, "then the lines on the spectrograph didn't make any sense at all."

For two years Schmidt struggled over the problem of the strange six lines on the spectrograph of 3C-273. Then, on February 5, 1963, Schmidt sat down to write a letter to a scientific journal. Suddenly his thoughts focused on the spectrograph, and he dug it out of the welter on his desk. "I took another look at the spectrum and noticed that if you ignored two of the lines, the other four looked rather regular, crowding together and getting weaker toward the blue end of the spectrum. I tried to express the relationship of one line to the other as a mathematical ratio."

In so doing, it seemed to Schmidt that the four lines represented those of hydrogen. If this were the case, they were in the wrong place for a star within our own galaxy. But assuming they were hydrogen lines, Schmidt did some fast arithmetic and calculated that the lines were red shifted by an amazing sixteen per cent. This meant that the "neighboring" star was not within our galaxy at all. Rather, it was one of the most distant objects ever seen. It was two billion light-years from the earth and racing away at more than twenty-seven thousand miles per second. That would mean that far from being a dim star, it was, to be seen at all, one of the brightest objects in the universe, spewing forth fantastic amounts of light and radio energies.

Now, with the key to interpretation in hand (assuming an enormous red shift) the other two lines of the 3C-273 spectrograph fell into place. One was an oxygen line, the other magnesium. The hunt was on to look at the spectra of other 3C radio sources.

The next object to be examined was 3C-48, actually the first of the strange new objects to be discovered. The lines of its spectrograph, never before deciphered, now yielded in about ten minutes to the extreme-red-shift idea. When they had all been identified, it appeared that 3C-48 was about twice as far away as 3C-273—about four billion light-years—and moving away at twice the speed.

The new and strange objects, called by Jesse Greenstein "perhaps the most bizarre and puzzling objects ever observed through a telescope," posed all sorts of questions. About two hundred have now

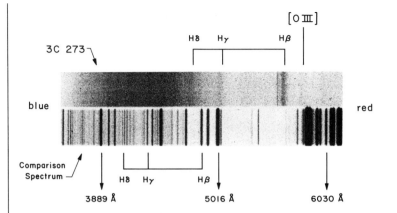

In the spectrogram of 3C-273 the hydrogen lines Hδ, Hγ, and Hβ are shown to be shifted far to the red end of the spectrum, compared to those in the spectrogram of a star within our own galaxy.

Chinese astronomers reported witnessing in 1054 A.D.
a supernova blaze in the constellation Taurus. The famous
Crab Nebula, shown here, is composed of material flung
outward at enormous speed by that stellar explosion.

been found, ranging from two to ten billion light-years away and pouring out prodigious amounts of energy. "At present, we have no accepted explanation of how so much energy can be generated," says Schmidt.

But astronomers did have a name for them—quasars, for quasi-stellar radio sources. One quasar was reckoned to be about two and a half trillion times as luminous as our own sun. Astronomers have calculated that to keep such an object at its current brightness for even a million years—a mere eye blink as they reckon time—matter equal to that contained in one hundred thousand suns would have to be converted to radiant energy.

When further observations indicated that the sources of these fantastic energies were far too small to be galaxies but rather were massive organizations of starlike objects, a number of theories were proposed to explain them. All were scrapped as most scientists agreed that such enormous energies could only be emitted by a catastrophe of cosmic proportions.

Yet what possible form could such a catastrophe take? The most awesome disaster man can envision is a collision of galaxies, a cosmic derailment as a train of stars sideswipes those of another galaxy. But even such a monstrous crash would produce only a candle glow compared with the arc-light energies emitted by the quasars, if they were billions of light-years away from the earth.

Other ideas were explored. A chain reaction of exploding stars was one, a cosmic string of firecrackers popping off in rapid succession until an entire galaxy had been detonated.

Such an idea required a galaxy constructed along lines never before seen in the heavens—a core of supernovas timed to explode one after the

The entire Filamentary Nebula in the constellation Cygnus may be the remains of a supernova explosion that was not recorded. *(California Institute of Technology)*

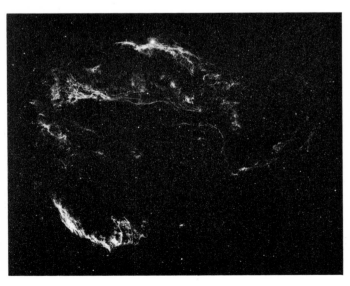

other and spaced so close together they could be set off at a rate of ten or so a year. But in our own galaxy such supernovas are seen barely once in two centuries.

Another idea envisioned a star of enormous size that had collapsed in upon itself until it reached a critical point and exploded instead of continuing on to become a white dwarf. The gravitational forces created by such an enormous mass falling in upon itself would turn the explosion inward, containing the energies and igniting still more complete conversion of matter to energy, and eventually achieving the tremendous blaze of a quasar. But no star could possibly attain such obesity without exploding long before reaching a size at which gravitational collapse could take place. The most massive stars known are only sixty-five times larger than our sun, and the order of magnitude required to achieve gravitational collapse is hundreds of thousands of times beyond that.

But there is one theory that has not as yet been explained away—antimatter. In a simplistic explanation, antimatter is what its name implies, the opposite of matter. Its existence was first postulated in 1928, by the British physicist Paul A. M. Dirac, who was trying to reconcile the quantum theory with Einstein's theory of relativity. The theoretical results of his studies led him to the disturbing conclusion that there must be a particle with the same mass as an electron but with a positive electrical charge instead of a negative one. An implication of this conclusion was that any nucleus surrounded by such positive electrons would have to be negatively charged. In short, the combination of positive electrons and a negative nucleus would be the exact antithesis of atoms as we know them—an antiatom.

The idea was preposterous to most scientists, and even Dirac admitted his unhappiness with the results, since the flabbergasting positive electron could be neither observed nor measured; it merely existed hypothetically as an affront to the evidence then available to experimental physics.

There matters stood for four years—an obvious impossibility had been made possible by the results of an authoritative theoretical study. Then, in 1932, Dirac's hypothesis was upheld by Dr. Carl Anderson, a physicist at Cal Tech. Anderson was studying cosmic rays, those mysterious high-energy particles that have always bombarded the earth from space. Cosmic rays enter our atmosphere at fantastic velocities, collide with its atoms, and shatter them into the detritus we know as subatomic particles. To record the nature of these particles, Anderson used a Wilson's cloud chamber—a container filled with an alcohol-saturated gas. A particle entering the chamber leaves a visible trail of droplets in the gas. A magnetic field set up in the chamber will push the particles along a curved path. From this curving necklace of droplets, the speed, mass, and charge of the particle can be measured.

In the course of photographing the track of the cosmic rays one day, Anderson made a startling discovery—a particle with the same mass as an electron had left its highly revealing footprints on the plate. But this was like no electron track ever before photographed, for its path in the magnetic field curved in a direction opposite to that of the negatively charged electrons. The meaning was unquestionable—this was photographic evidence of an electron with a positive charge. Anderson dubbed it the positron, for it was the same oddly behaved positive electron that Dirac had predicted.

The discovery of the positron, instead of throwing physics into a quandary by its heretical behavior, offered tangible proof of yet another mathematician's work. Albert Einstein's theory of relativity and its equation $E = mc^2$, which states that matter is simply congealed energy and can be transformed back into energy, suddenly had demonstrable proof in the form of the positron. For the positron was doomed to extinction the instant it met its opposite number, the electron. In collision, the two antithetical particles were annihilated and released fantastic energies in the process, energies that conform exactly to the Einstein formula.

Besides offering demonstrable proof of abstruse mathematical formulae, the positron sent physicists scurrying to find other antiparticles. Their discovery would help confirm the essential symmetry of all nature. This belief, originated by the Greeks, could only be upheld in the face of the newly discovered positron by assuming that every particle had its own exact counterpart in the form of an antiparticle. Protons must have antiprotons, neutrons, antineutrons, and the growing number of elementary particles being discovered by the experimental nuclear physicists all had to have a mirror in which their antimatter counterparts could be pictured.

Physicists reasoned that the antiproton had an existence that was virtual rather than real. That is, they could predict it, but only by shattering atomic nuclei and, in the process, converting some of the energy released into a tangible antiproton, could its existence actually be proved. However, there was an energy barrier that had to be hurdled. A proton is a heavy particle, nearly two thousand times more massive than an electron. To fabricate the antithesis of such a particle, the antiproton, calls

164

for a tremendous surge of power—a burst of energy that physicists calculated at six billion electron volts. An atom smasher of such power simply did not exist.

In 1954 the compelling lure of the antiproton resulted in the building of the bevatron—a six-billion-electron-volt atom smasher—at the University of California. Its main task was to find the antiproton.

With the price of atom smashers then pegged at about one million dollars a BEV (billion electron volts), some scientists thought the project a ridiculous waste of research funds. One eminent physicist went so far as to label the search for an antiproton nonsense and backed his opinion with a $500 bet.

The proton accelerator called the bevatron began operations in 1954 and ten years later underwent major modifications that increased its proton output by four times. *(Lawrence Radiation Laboratory, Berkeley, California)*

165

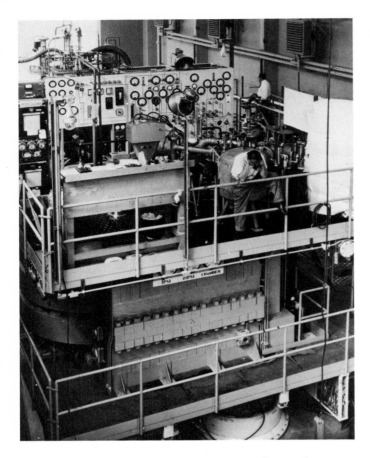

This seventy-two-inch bubble chamber is used to analyze the subatomic debris from nuclear collisions in the bevatron. Filled with liquid hydrogen, it records the tracks of nuclear particles, which provide scientists with important information about the mass, size, charge, and velocity of particles. *(Lawrence Radiation Laboratory, Berkeley, California)*

He paid off in 1955 when Emilio Segrè and Owen Chamberlain, two University of California physicists, produced an antiproton with their expensive "nuc-cracker."

Now the proton had its mate in the antiproton, and things were looking up, or was it down, in the antimatter derby. Bevatrons of even greater power than the one at Berkeley were built, and each began shattering atoms and littering the fields of physical theory with a confusing proliferation of subatomic particles that were part of the proton and neutron or elements of the glue that bound these nucleonic components together. And for each of the so-called elementary particles that was found—including such exotic specimens as mu-mesons, pi-mesons, and hyperons—there was a corresponding antiparticle produced in the atom smasher or predicted mathematically. No one, however, had even attempted to fit antimatter into the existing theories of the creation of the universe. There were several popular theories, each with its adherents and detractors who agreed on but one point—the universe was basically symmetrical. With the discovery of the antiproton, Maurice Goldhaber, an eminent physicist at the Brookhaven National Laboratory on Long Island, declared, "Some of the current theories of the origin of matter tacitly or explicitly assume an asymmetry in the process of 'creation'—that is, the creation of nucleons, but not antinucleons."

And so it was. One theory held that in the beginning there was a dense, neutron-rich atmosphere called the 'ylem,' which by a process called neutron capture and beta decay was transformed into the elements that make up our universe.

A second theory held that there was really no

beginning, middle, or end to the universe. The galaxies of the cosmos remain at a constant number, with new galaxies being formed as soon as old ones disappear. This so-called steady-state theory insisted that hydrogen, the basic building block of all matter, is continually being formed in the void. The virginal hydrogen is then molded by gravitational forces into new stars and eventually galaxies.

The big-bang idea, of course, benefits most from the antimatter theories. Goldhaber took antimatter and made it a condition of creation. By so doing, he preserved the physicist's jealously guarded doctrine of symmetry and, at the same time, modified the big-bang theory. "We shall assume," he said, "that there existed at first a single particle containing the mass of the whole universe, which we shall call here the 'universon.' We shall further assume that at a time unknown at present, the universon divided into a particle and its antiparticle, which we shall call the 'cosmon' and the 'anticosmon,' each possessing a large 'nucleonic charge,' but of opposite sign (where nucleonic charge is defined as $+1$ for a nucleon and $—1$ for an antinucleon). The cosmon and the anticosmon similarly may have flown apart with a large relative velocity. After the separation, the cosmon, which replaces Lemaître's idea of a primeval atom and must, therefore, be assumed to be the particle of positive nucleonic charge, 'decayed,' possibly through many intermediate steps, into nucleons, which in turn formed our present expanding cosmos."

Goldhaber did not at the time know whether to postulate that the other half of his universon, the anticosmon, also decayed to form an anticosmos

Photographic tracks in a liquid-hydrogen bubble chamber show the results of the collision of an incoming antiproton with a proton in the liquid hydrogen. The diagram at left sketches the path of the antiproton and of the particles and antiparticles produced by the collision. (Brookhaven National Laboratory)

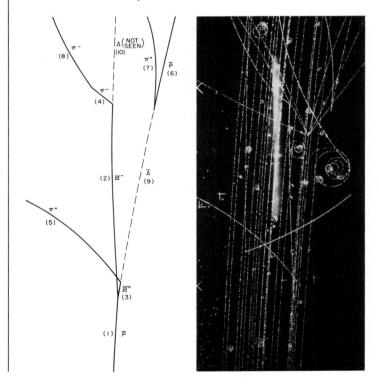

or antiuniverse, and he admitted his speculations raised many questions that might "ultimately prove answerable by observation."

The 21st century may provide those answers, but even now the newly discovered quasars are offering clues and underlining the possibilities of Goldhaber's cosmology. There is yet another view of the creation, which incorporates antimatter even more faithfully than the Lemaître-Goldhaber model and at the same time offers an explanation of the quasars.

This is the so-called Klein-Alfvén model, the work of a pair of Swedish physicists, Oskar Klein and Hannes Alfvén. In explaining the theory, Alfvén first disposes of the big-bang idea by saying: "If the original nucleon had contained antimatter as well as matter it would have annihilated itself; the big bang would have been a too big bang!"

The Swedish physicists view the creation from the starting point of an immense, extremely dilute cloud of gas—a plasma composed of electrified particles. "Let us call it an ambiplasma," says Alfvén, "because it contained both particles and antiparticles." The cloud of plasma was assumed to be in the form of an immense sphere some trillion light-years across. Within such a sphere particles and antiparticles would almost never encounter one another. But then the cloud begins to contract, and although the particles are still widely separated, now and then a proton and an antiproton collide, and their mutual annihilation releases energy, mostly in the form of radiation. As the cloud continues to contract, collisions become more and more frequent. When the radius of the cloud has shrunk to about a billion light-years, the radiation arising from particle-antiparticle annihila-

Dr. Fred Hoyle, the British astronomer who postulated the theory of the steady-state universe, in which hydrogen atoms are continuously created in interstellar space at a rate compensating for the rate of expansion of the universe, so that its average density remains the same.

Dr. Maurice Goldhaber, director of the Brookhaven National Laboratory. *Brookhaven National Laboratory)*

tion is so strong that it overcomes gravitational attraction. The cloud, including the galaxies that have condensed within it by that time, begins to expand. The result is the expanding universe we now observe with our telescopes.

As proof of the validity of such a theory Alfvén points out that the energies unleashed within the magnetic field of the ambiplasma will emit radio waves. "Hence," says Alfvén, "radio telescopes offer the best chance of detecting an ambiplasma in space if it exists. They would record such a radiating source as a radio star. Here may be an explanation for the mysterious quasars, which emit enormous amounts of radio energy. It seems quite possible that some, if not all, of the starlike radio objects in the heavens, including quasars, arise from matter-antimatter annihilations."

Alfvéns's highly creative explanation of creation and the quasars has caused a good deal of controversy among astronomers and physicists—controversy that may not be resolved until the 21st century. But many do agree that the quasars may give us an extraordinary view of what might have happened when the universe was very young. They believe that the light we now receive from some of the farthermost quasars must have blazed forth when the universe was in its infancy, assuming, as most experts do, that the universe is approximately thirteen billion years old.

In one sense this peering backward across time to the beginning is like running a film backward. Our new astronomical tools enable us in effect to run the film record of cosmic events backward until eventually we may be able to perceive the actual act of creation or come close enough to it to deduce the actual happening.

"The quasars," says Allan Sandage, "seem to

tell us that the universe was more closely packed billions of years ago than it is today. The speed at which they are flying apart indicates that they were all back in one spot some ten to thirteen billion years ago. That's when the big bang might have taken place."

The idea of a gigantic explosion as the wellspring of the universe fascinates a Princeton physicist named Robert Dicke, who says, "If in fact the universe began with a big bang, it would have to have been an explosion on an enormous scale. The flash produced would be unbelievably brilliant, enough light to fill what was then a much smaller universe. Thus, at least a residue of the light should be around."

This would seem to be the final proof needed for the big-bang theory to be accepted. But how do you pick out what is now, thirteen billion years later, a whimpering residue from the granddaddy of all explosions? The one hope scientists had of finding such a radiation residue was the fact that if the universe was indeed expanding, light from the big bang would now have been traveling for some thirteen billion years. Thus, it too, like the quasars, galaxies, and stars, would be red shifted, so much so that it would no longer be received as light waves. It would be in the form of radio waves.

These ideas could be expressed in complex mathematical equations, but actual proof would have to be observational and there matters rested until the spring of 1965. Then, a pair of Bell Telephone Laboratories scientists, Arno Penzias and Robert Wilson, ran into trouble. An antenna originally designed to pick up signals reflected from Echo, a communications satellite, was instead receiving a strange crackling noise that Penzias and Wilson could not identify. The antenna, on a hilltop

Dr. Robert H. Dicke, a professor of physics at Princeton University. *(Ulli Steltzer)*

170

in Holmdel, New Jersey, was dismantled, cleaned, and put back together. The crackling persisted. It was residual radio noise coming from a completely unidentifiable source.

The engineers at Bell Labs had radio signals with no explanation of where they might have originated. The physicists at Princeton had a theory but no proof. It was inevitable that they should get together. Since then four other locations have recorded the mysterious crackling noise, and the Princeton group believes that these signals are radio energy from "a primeval fireball" of radiation, surviving from the earliest days of the universe.

Dicke's idea does not stop simply with a big bang. Rather, he foresees a universe that expands and collapses in on itself to the point where it lights off the big bang. Thus the creation follows the death of the universe in a recurring cycle, so that life itself may be a reflection of the bringing forth and dissolution of the universe. What then is the true account—big bang, expansion and contraction, or antimatter—of the creation? Whatever the explanation, the universe is so vast, so complex, and so varied, man will probably never find all the answers. But in the 21st century, that may not be too important. It may be that what is really vital is simply to ask the right questions.

171

Index